THE STORY OF FRITZ HABER

The Story of
Fritz Haber

✠ ✠ ✠

Morris Goran

UNIVERSITY OF OKLAHOMA PRESS
NORMAN

BY MORRIS GORAN

Introduction to Physical Science (Glencoe, 1959)
Experimental Biology for Boys (New York, 1961)
Experimental Chemistry for Boys (New York, 1961)
Experimental Astronautics (Indianapolis, 1967)
The Story of Fritz Haber (Norman, 1967)

The paper on which this book is printed bears the watermark of the University of Oklahoma Press and has an effective life of at least three hundred years.

85472

LIBRARY OF CONGRESS CATALOG CARD NUMBER: 67-24615

Copyright 1967 by the University of Oklahoma Press, Publishing Division of the University. Composed and printed at Norman, Oklahoma, U.S.A., by the University of Oklahoma Press. First Edition.

For My Three Girls,
Cymia, Marjorie, and Ruth

✠

Preface

✠

ALMOST ANY PERSON in the Western world born in the nineteenth century and living through a decade or more of the twentieth has witnessed the transformation of a gaslight, horse-and-buggy society into one with a wealth of technological achievement. Man's age-old problems of cold, hunger, disease, communication, and transportation seemed to be on their way to solution as telephone, telegraph, synthetic drugs, automobile, synthetic fertilizer, radio, and airplane came to the fore. The flourishing of pure science at the same time indicated the possibility that it was the bulwark of and the necessity for this change. Perhaps unrelated, the monarchies and despotisms of the past gave way to more popularly based governments.

Fritz Haber was among the few persons fortunate to be near the focal point of the transformation. He was recognized as the authority in the relations between science and industry, science and government, and science in the support of war and peace. An English scientist, J. D. Bernal, in his book *The Social Function of Science* (1939), called him "the greatest authority in the world on the relations between scientific research and industry."

Haber was active in almost every branch of chemical research. In itself, this would be sufficient to earn him a place in the records of science. But he was an expert, too, in today's vexing problems of research organization.

His life was filled with dramatic adventure. His famous nitrogen-fixation system was developed in competition with another scientist. His patriotism for Germany brought him the contempt of many when he developed and advocated the use of poison gas in World War I and the smug smirk of some when he searched the seas for gold in order to pay his country's war debts. To be rewarded with exile by Hitler's Germany was one of the last smarting blows to his efforts. Even then, there were malicious whispers that he could have embraced the Nazi ideology if it had not been for his Jewish background. Few patriots of his stature have ever been so treated; and no exile has thereafter risen to higher esteem within the country from which he was banned—indeed, to a position of honor by all mankind.

MORRIS GORAN

Lincolnwood, Illinois
September 12, 1967

✠

Contents

✠

ix

✠

Illustrations

✠

THE STORY OF FRITZ HABER

✠

I. The Early Years

✠

In 1868 the man who would become Wilhelm II of Germany was nine years old. His grandmother, Queen Victoria of England, had reigned thirty-one years, and Franz Josef of Austria had been a monarch for twenty. Napoleon III was emperor of France and would-be emperor Maximilian had been executed by a firing squad in Mexico. Andrew Johnson was president of the thirty-seven united states of America. Richard Wagner's *Die Meistersinger* was performed, Leo Tolstoi had finished his *War and Peace*, Charles Dickens was working on *Mystery of Edwin Drood,* and Karl Marx's first volume of *Das Kapital* had already been published. Thomas Edison was twenty-one years old, Henry Ford was five, and Wilbur Wright was one year old.

In 1868, Siegfried Haber and Company was an established Breslau organization dealing in pigments and dyestuffs. The company merchandised natural dyestuffs, resins, linseed oil, whale oil, and industrial fats; it was one of Germany's largest importers of natural indigo. The founder, who had given the company his name, had worked diligently to develop his business. He told his children that "the blood came out from under my fingernails" because of his arduous labor. Actually, his hard work was involved

3

with long hours, efforts to establish fruitful contacts, travel, and correspondence; it was not physical labor as such.

Siegfried Haber's helper and supporter was his beautiful and young wife, Paula, who was also his first cousin, the youngest of his Uncle Julius' ten children. Their marriage was shortlived, however, for on December 9, 1868, she died in childbirth. The child, Fritz, survived.

During Fritz Haber's first nine years he had several substitute mothers: his Aunt Ida and Aunt Ulrica, his grandmothers, and a kind housekeeper, Miss Wohlgemuth. When he was nine years old, his father married again. Siegfried Haber's second wife was nineteen-year-old Hedwig Hamburger, whom he had met when she was visiting relatives in Breslau.

The boy came to love his young stepmother and as one expression of his sentiment gave her white lilacs every Christmastime. The household grew until Fritz had three sisters to give him ample additional affection; yet he was ten years older than his eldest stepsister.

When he was old enough for formal schooling, Fritz was enrolled at the *Volksschule,* or common school. After three years, he went to the St. Elizabeth Gymnasium for nine years.

The curriculum at the Gymnasium centered about the humanities. Students were required to learn Latin, Greek, literature, and philosophy. The little science taught was a rough mixture of religion, philosophy, and nature study called natural history. As a consequence, Fritz developed an interest in literature and philosophy which he maintained throughout his life. Goethe became his favorite poet and Kant his favorite philosopher. Amid the rising nationalism, they were almost unavoidable choices.

With Hans Trentin (who was to become a mayor of Bres-

4

lau), Albert Neisser (a future skin specialist), Paul and Richard Ehrlich (later to be architects), Ernst "Hünchen" Hamburger (his stepmother's cousin), Fritz Lasch, and Karl Czapski, Fritz became a member of the Academic Literary Society. After school hours, these young men memorized long sections of Goethe's works, read Greek classics for fun, and held lengthy discussions about the good life.

Men of Fritz Haber's generation believed intensely in progress and enlightenment through the acquisition of culture. Fritz even attempted to saturate his little sisters with languages and good literature. When he was sixteen years old, many times he arrayed the youngsters, aged two, four, and six, side by side and proceeded to recite Greek odes to them to accustom them to the harmony of the Greek language. The young man was also a dramatist. Hardly a family party or New Year's Eve affair was without a skit of his—frequently he was writer, producer, and one of the actors.

On the other hand he seemed to have little interest in music—perhaps the only subject which failed to catch his attention—and this despite the fact that the University of Breslau awarded Johannes Brahms an honorary degree when Fritz was twelve. Indeed, the city of Breslau was honored when the composer conducted the first performance of his "Academic Festival Overture." (Eight years later the university missed its opportunity to confer a doctorate upon Charles Proteus Steinmetz. His dissertation had been accepted, but he was a socialist agitator and the police were after him. Steinmetz escaped to Switzerland and then to the United States, where he became a distinguished industrial scientist and mathematician.)

Fritz was afforded other opportunities for personal development. Every summer the family took a vacation trip, usually to the Alps or Italy, and becoming more familiar with the art treasures of the Continent, especially of Italy, was always part of the vacation activities.

The boy was also growing physically, and during his seventeenth summer, spent with his parents in Austria, his large appetite necessitated special negotiations by his father. The innkeeper demanded, and received, extra payment to cover the expense of boarding young Haber.

In the autumn of 1886, when he was not quite eighteen, Fritz Haber enrolled in the University of Berlin, the home of such celebrated scientists and scholars as Rudolf Virchow, Hermann Helmholtz, and Theodor Mommsen. Six thousand students attended courses in all branches of learning. They participated, too, in extracurricular activities, such as parading on the eve of the pageant for the ninetieth birthday of Wilhelm I, March 22, 1887.

The main building of the school was once the residence of Prince Henry, brother of Frederick the Great. The university structure was built around three sides of a court open southward to the street. A high ornamental iron fence guarded the entrance which contained white marble statues of the brothers Humboldt.

The elective system of the university enabled Haber to sample offerings of several departments. But he soon became especially stimulated by chemistry. At fifteen, he had burned towels to see what would happen. His father had recognized a tendency to experiment and consented to more enlightening work in the attic. Economic factors heightened the interest. The once-flourishing wool trade and the growing sugar-beet industry of Silesia gave prestige to chemists in Breslau. A knowledge of chemistry was beneficial too in his father's business. Furthermore, toward the latter part of of the nineteenth century, a wave of scientific research swept over Germany. The outstanding chemists of the world were German.

The chief attractions in the physical sciences at the University of Berlin were Professors Hermann Helmholtz and August Wilhelm Hofmann. Helmholtz was an outstanding physicist and physiologist as well as a lucid thinker about the philosophy and methodology of science. He believed that the principles of classical mechanics devised by Isaac Newton was a key to understanding nature. As a young man of twenty-six, he was an independent co-discoverer of the first law of thermodynamics, the principle that describes the energy content of any system as being constant regardless of changes within the system. He thought the procedure of scientists could be encompassed in the words *preparation, illumination,* and *verification.* Hofmann had first been a student of philology and law, then he became an expert linguist, and finally he turned to mathematics, physics, and chemistry. He discovered aniline in coal tar, initiating the coal-tar industry.

Helmholtz spoke so softly that his words were barely audible. Although the calculations he performed on the blackboard were elucidating, his course was too difficult. He took for granted, even from beginning students, a measure of preliminary work as well as an extraordinary understanding. He was the counterpart of the present-day research professors who are more absorbed in their research problems than in classroom duties.

Hofmann was the more inspiring teacher for Haber. He used demonstrations with his lectures and had a more revealing sequence of topics; his course was more carefully planned. Yet Hofmann's demonstrations were prepared by his assistants; he lacked the manual dexterity to be a good laboratory technician. At times he told his graduate stu-

7

THE STORY OF FRITZ HABER

dents that in his student days all his fingers operated like thumbs, and thus he could not hold a test tube very long without "scrunching" it. Haber's small hands and fingers made him a candidate for a similar experience.

Fritz left the University of Berlin at the end of his first semester, but not because of real dissatisfaction. It was the vogue during his student years to attend several universities. Heidelberg was the next stop in his academic journey, and he remained there for one and one-half years. Like many other students, he acquired a scar on his face from a duel —a brand presumably indicating higher education, a badge of honor resulting from a test of character and stamina. Hazing in United States college fraternities during the early twentieth century is but a meager parallel to the duelling practices of nineteenth-century German university students. Duelling represented status.

In 1887, Professor Robert Bunsen of Heidelberg University was seventy-six years old. He had taught chemistry for more than fifty years, establishing an enviable reputation. His lectures were intensely practical and factual. Often he would inform his classes that one chemical fact properly established was worth more than all the theories one could invent. He insisted, too, upon a thorough training in mathematics and physics, claiming, "A chemist who is not also a a physicist is worthless."

Haber was influenced by Bunsen. He, too, became practical and factual; his inclination toward physics and mathematics became more pronounced. One of the courses he enjoyed was calculus, taught by Bunsen's good friend, Dr. Leo Koenigsberger.

Leaving Heidelberg, Haber returned to Breslau for military service, for during the nineteenth century every major country in Europe had compulsory military training. In

8

Germany, young men enrolled in higher schools of learning needed to serve but one year instead of the two or three years ordinarily required. An army ruling in force since the Napoleonic wars allowed all males who had successfully finished six years in a secondary school the privilege of only one years' military service; the opportunity to become an officer was afforded the more highly educated. Large numbers of boys sought the required schooling solely to take advantage of these concessions; thus the ruling became somewhat of a boon to education.

Haber joined the artillery regiment stationed at Breslau, where he rapidly won the respect of experienced soldiers. Although he was a novice, the men in his regiment came to ask him questions. No doubt their respect stemmed from the fact that he was given the task of surveying the sector about Breslau—from boyhood he had been acquainted with every path and house in the area because the family home was in the district of Scheidnich. The year's service also included academic lectures. These, enjoyed by Haber, were on philosophy and were held in the stable, the cavalry house, with no thought of influencing the nonprimate occupants.

On October 16, 1889, he entered Charlottenburg *Technische Hochschule*. This institution had been established in 1799 as a small trade school and had grown to be the largest engineering college in Germany. Since 1884 it had occupied a huge building in a beautiful section of Berlin. In 1889, the school had a faculty of about 150 and more than 4,000 students, among them a significant number of army and navy officers.

Haber had many friends his own age in Berlin. His cousin George Spiro was studying to become an oculist. His older cousin Ernst Spiro was already entrenched in law. A good friend was August Marx, a student of the humanities. Paul

9

Askenasy and Richard Abegg, also from Breslau, were fellow chemistry students at the engineering school.

A stimulating course in the chemical technology of fibrous materials was given by O. N. Witt. Karl Liebermann, one of the co-synthesizers of alizarin, a red dyestuff formerly obtained from the root of the madder plant, was another enterprising and effective teacher. With his guidance, Fritz Haber entered the realm of chemical research.

His first study, helping Liebermann, involved a material related to indigo. The results were published in an authoritative journal, *Berichte der Deutschen Chemische Gesellschaft*, commonly called the *Berichte*. In the following volume the journal published Haber's doctoral dissertation, which concerned a substance, piperonal, also related to indigo. For the research he had treated the compound with many other substances and had isolated and characterized each new formation. Publication of his work, however, was not a mark of recognition; it was an expected procedure.

Early in 1891, Haber was awarded the degree of Doctor of Philosophy, barely passing his final oral examination. A. W. Hofmann, Karl Rammelsberg, August Kundt, and Wilhelm Dilthey were his examiners. Hofmann, his former teacher, was from the parent university of the Charlottenburg school of engineering and the others were from the *Technische Hochschule*. Haber's philosophy, they said, "went brilliantly," but "he was ignorant of resistance measurements of electrolytes."

2. Rejection and a New Beginning

IN 1891, Wilhelm Ostwald and his newly established Institute for Physical Chemistry in Leipzig became a scientific attraction. Young chemists made Leipzig their goal; Ostwald and his school promised new and exciting laboratory adventures. Ostwald not only made singular advances in support of physical chemistry but also helped establish the philosophy of science as an academic subject. In both areas of knowledge he was not so much an original thinker as he was a publicist. His efforts in philosophy of science went to the extreme at times. He declared energy to be the basic substance of the universe and dealt with mental energy and its transformation; he even devised a formula for happiness involving expenditure of energy in accordance with volitions and desires.

Fritz Haber wanted to work with Ostwald. Besides, his father's closest brother, Julius, and his family—a wife and daughter—lived in Leipzig. Julius Haber was an established attorney, who was later to become president of the German Association of Lawyers and a judge in the highest court of the land.

Karl Liebermann, an organic chemist, did not encourage his students to enter physical chemistry, notwithstanding its increasing popularity. He advocated the study of the com-

11

pounds of carbon as a tested discipline, a founder of new industries, and a key to understanding life processes. Since the eventful year of 1828 when German chemist Friedrich Wöhler had synthesized urea from ammonium thiocyanate, organic chemistry had been largely a German development to which the great Justus Leibig had contributed, as had Haber's teachers, including Liebermann. Of what use was measuring minute quantities or working with electrical apparatus? Haber evidently saw his future in the latter kind of work. But Ostwald did not see a future for him; he was turned down at Leipzig.

In 1891 employment for a young scientist was limited. Schools took only the very best students to train for professorships. Most of the more than five thousand chemical factories in Germany did not need doctors of philosophy. Fritz Haber had to leave Germany for employment.

His first position, which he held almost a year, was at a Budapest distillery, Leipziger, belonging to a friend of his father's. Here the only accomplishment he could later recall was the invention of a complicated apparatus enabling him to take aging alcohol for personal use. For several months he was with a fertilizer factory near Auschwitz in Galicia. Then came several weeks with a textile company, Feldmühle. He was an unpaid junior clerk at all three places. He was given only routine tasks to perform and was not expected to make judgments. These minor duties did not satisfy his curiosity or his creative urge.

After leaving industry and before deciding his future course, he rested at a sanatorium for a few weeks. During some school holidays he had stayed at these resorts. They were soothing and peaceful, good for the strains of excessive work and study as well as for overindulgence in liquor and tobacco. At school, social pressures encouraged drinking. Many students, despite a decided inability to drink intoxicating beverages, either conformed or were forced to do so by older classmates. Fritz Haber was no exception. He had to become acclimated to the drinking patterns of the student, the military man, and the industrial worker. Once he got so drunk that he walked through a glass door in his father's house. He was cut by the glass, but the accident marked the last time he became intoxicated.

In 1892, Haber entered the Federal Polytechnical School at Zurich, Switzerland. The school boasted of a long list of successful graduates; employers often came to it for well-trained and diligent men. Haber came especially to study under Professor Georg Lunge, who was highly respected as a teacher and analytical chemist. Also born in Breslau, Lunge had been a student of Bunsen's. He had subsequently gone to England, where he had stayed twelve years before returning to the Continent.

Haber studied seven subjects in his semester's stay at Zurich. Six were directly concerned with physical science and technology; they included "The Theory of Organic Dyes," "Glass and Pottery Manufacture," and "Technical Applications of Geology." The seventh subject, an elective divorced from his speciality, was "Philosophy of the Nineteenth Century." He spent much time in Lunge's laboratory learning about textiles, bleaching, dyeing, pigments, synthetic dyestuffs, inorganic technology, and metallurgy. Thus he became better equipped for employment. He had an advanced education that few others at the time possessed; it was not customary then to undertake additional study after attaining the doctorate.

While waiting for a good opportunity for employment, Fritz joined his father's organization. The elder Haber had established and developed his company through arduous and sacrificial work. Coming to the near-zenith of the business world after struggle and hardship, he believed in that procedure for the cultivation of self-reliance. He believed, furthermore, in duplicating or attempting to simulate the same rough road for his son.

One of Siegfried's first demands was that Fritz, aged twenty-four and with a doctorate in chemistry, take lessons to improve his handwriting. To a young man recently returned from association with the wisdom of the world and holding the highest academic degree, handwriting lessons were a smarting blow. But he acceded to his father's wishes; he practiced writing. His penmanship improved, and he became proud of the accomplishment. Even when past sixty, he still wrote a fine hand.

Siegfried Haber also made his son a traveling salesman; this was to be a good way for him to meet customers and learn the business. But Fritz, given the Hamburg territory, was displeased.

Father and son clashed at home and in the office. The latter was pioneering and adventurous; the former, having arrived, was settled and conservative. Their temperaments were not matched, and Fritz Haber was not inclined to adjust to staid ways. His stepmother, who had a good understanding of the differences between father and son, was an effective arbitrator, as was his Uncle Hermann, his mother's eldest brother. A success in business, as well as a civic leader and city councilman, Uncle Hermann became a confidant and adviser of Fritz. Both stepmother and uncle were probably aware of an underlying psychological problem. Siegfried Haber had lost his first wife through his son's birth. Whatever incipient hostile emotion existed as a result of this loss was heightened and brought to a head by a long series of petty business conflicts.

14

Not long after beginning his six-month stay in the business, chemist Fritz Haber realized that natural dyes would soon become obsolete. The company could not be successfully operated in the future, he figured, unless synthetic dyes were also stocked. In 1868 his former teacher, Karl Liebermann, had contributed to bankrupting the madder plantations in Alsace, southern France, and Algiers by his synthesis, with a fellow chemist, of the red dyestuff, alizarin. When artificial indigo was developed in the laboratory several years later, natural dyes were already yielding to the materials made in test tubes and retorts. Haber vigorously supported the opinion that synthetics were on the way in and that every progressive chemical sales establishment should stock them. His father was shocked by this point of view and called him a fool. Siegfried Haber did not believe in the artificial product and maintained that potential users, Polish and Russian dyers, would not like the innovation. But with time and pressure, he painfully acquiesced to the new trends, and the company began to sell synthetics.

During the summer of 1892 came the immediate cause for the business parting of father and son. A cholera epidemic had engulfed the port of Hamburg. The only treatment, found effective through rough trial and error, was chloride of lime. Siegfried Haber and Company sold chloride of lime. Young Haber, believing that the epidemic would spread before physicians could geographically isolate it, saw an opportunity for immense profits. He persuaded his father to purchase large quantities of chloride of lime in anticipation of large sales. But the epidemic was isolated and the Habers were left with huge stocks of the chemical. The elder Haber was furious. Aroused and bitter, he advised his son to retire to the academic world. "Go to a university," he said. "You don't belong in business!"

Fritz Haber desperately needed something to bolster his self-confidence. An antidote was necessary for a not-too-brilliant academic record, a lack of real success in private industry, and the involuntary exit from his father's business. In the absence of positive accomplishments, he became despondent. He began to doubt his abilities and his future. It was a period of despair; in this state, he continued to seek and dangle.

He went to Ludwig Knorr's laboratory at the University of Jena. One inducement was the presence of his friend Siegfried Czapski, who had a position as assistant to the renowned physicist Ernst Abbe at the optical works of Carl Zeiss. Another was the reputation of Knorr in organic chemistry—he had synthesized the medicinal substance, antipyrine. An additional and not inconsiderable factor was the standing of Jena in academic circles.

In the fall of 1892, Haber became an assistant in Knorr's laboratory. For three semesters he endured his laboratory lackey position. "Endured" because he began to hate the tasks—the endless routine of mixing reagents and purification of products; the monotony of mixing, heating, distilling, and crystallizing. "Lackey" because he had little chance for creative work; his main duties were to follow directions given by Knorr. The tangible result of his stay was a publication about an unimportant organic compound. Through differentiating chemical tests and subsequent inferences, Knorr and he had determined the arrangement in space of the atoms making up the molecule of the material.

Knorr was not impressed by Haber. Had Knorr thought well of him and his work, Haber would have been promoted —or at least have been happier. When a friend chided him with, "How long will you remain in this hole doing crystallizations?" he had more stimulation for leaving.

The story of his ultimately securing a satisfactory position was a favorite that he later told and retold. He had been attending a sick friend in Jena with sincere devotion, keeping almost constant vigil during the last days of his friend's life. The latter's brother heard of his Samaritanism and of his desire to leave Jena. He suggested that Fritz apply at the Karlsruhe *Technische Hochschule* in the Duchy of Baden, near the Franco-German border about fifty miles from Heidelberg. There an influential relative of the deceased friend would welcome him and help him to secure a good position. Haber sought out the man and found him to be the school janitor.

The story may have been meant to indicate that he had gained a lowly job. A better explanation for Haber's application at Karlsruhe was that his friend August Marx was teaching in a local high school. Furthermore, the Karlsruhe Engineering College was outstanding in chemical technology. In 1885, Heinrich Hertz, twenty-eight years old, had devised in his laboratory at Karlsruhe an electrical oscillator setting up an energy that displayed all the properties of visible light; he had verified the electromagnetic theory of light, first suggested by English scientist James Clerk Maxwell about twenty years prior.

Haber secured an appointment to see one of the professors, Hans Bunte, who received him coldly and was hardly interested in his qualifications. But Haber persisted, and in the end, he received an appointment as assistant in the Department of Chemical and Fuel Technology.

The Karlsruhe *Technische Hochschule* was founded in 1825 and enlarged in 1832. By 1833, Karl F. Nebenius, minister of the interior in the Grand Duchy of Baden, could write: "National wealth can be increased in no better way than by spreading abroad useful scientific knowledge. A higher technical education breaks down the prejudice against manual labor; technical training should be rated at par with university training. Scientific education gives a cultural training peculiar to itself but as valuable as the culture resulting from classical training."

The dichotomy between engineering and the classics persisted throughout the nineteenth century. Zurich was the only technical school on the Continent in which a university atmosphere and a high level of culture were being maintained. This was a result of trying to satisfy advocates of both an engineering school and a university. According to the charters issued, both were to have been established; but difficulties arose and only one school was built.

Germany nonetheless developed technical schools. In a section such as Saxony, with about four million inhabitants, there were at the beginning of the century 112 *Fortbildungsschulen,* 39 *Höhere Industrieschulen,* 44 business colleges, 11 agricultural schools, and 25 technical schools for women and girls; all were under government control. The lowest type of technical training school was the *Fortbildungsschule,* or continuation school. It served as a supplement to elementary academic work. A grade higher were the *Höhere Industrieschulen* and *Technische Fachschulen;* on the same level were schools meant for single trades. Often cities became known for the skill and excellence of special schools. The tanner's school at Freiburg, the one for coppersmiths at Hanover, that for clockmakers at Furtwangen, and one for woodworkers at Berchtesgaden were renowned.

The acme of the special technical schools were the *Technische Hochschulen,* or institutes of technology. Often associated with universities, they were governed by a head rector and a senate composed of ranking faculty members.

Like universities, they were divided into departments, each with its own chairman, *Abteilungs-Vorsteher*. A student in any of the divisions paid an annual tuition ranging from 300 to 350 marks (70 to 80 dollars).

In 1894, the Karlsruhe Engineering College, with about twelve hundred students, had separate buildings for its architecture, forestry, civil, mechanical, electrical, and chemical engineering divisions. Together with an administration building and a library, these buildings were arranged about an open court. Adjacent new structures housed the electricity and chemistry departments, the power plant, and an extensive greenhouse. At the center of the court was a bust of a great engineer, Ferdinand Redtenbacher, who had died in 1867. Before the main edifice were life-size statues of astronomer Johannes Kepler and philosopher Erwin, often called Erwin von Steinbach.

Full professors in the chemistry and chemical engineering divisions were Karl Engler and Hans Bunte. Engler, with one eye almost closed, was respected for his excellent judgment and knowledge of his specialties, oil and oxidation. He was a visionary, who became interested in the new phenomenon of radioactivity. In 1905 he predicted a vast new energy source when man could exploit the spontaneously disintegrating atoms. The discovery of radioactivity was one of the three laboratory events during 1895–1905 which, together with the quantum and relativity theories, propounded by Germans Max Planck and Albert Einstein, ushered in twentieth-century physical science. The electron was isolated in England by Sir Joseph John Thomson, X rays were discovered in Germany by Wilhelm Konrad Röntgen, and radioactivity was first found in France by Antoine Henri Becquerel.

Hans Bunte was a less impressive personality. An aristocrat in appearance and manner, he almost always dressed in formal clothes, wearing the knee-length Prince Albert coat. One colleague of Haber's suggested that the young instructor unwittingly adopted some of Bunte's mannerisms.

Bunte prompted Haber's first study at Karlsruhe, the breakdown by heat of that class of compounds called hydrocarbons. These are the most numerous of the several million known chemical compounds, two or more elements joined in a definite and fixed composition by weight. The 104 fundamental building blocks of matter—elements—combine with one another in many ways, but no other two elements approach the versatility of combination of carbon and hydrogen. The wealth of actual and possible combinations of the two elements indicates that they are most suitably mated. Inharmonious unions of the two exist, but what happy union does not have its discord? There are hydrocarbons whose carbon units are joined to make an open-chain molecule, an aliphatic structure. There are hydrocarbons whose carbon atoms are tied together to make a ring molecule, an aromatic compound. The aliphatics and aromatics can be grouped into numerous subsidiary classes. Haber was not concerned with any special class. He sought a general rule for decomposition through heat and experimented with several different kinds of hydrocarbons. He perfected some faulty analytical techniques and established a basic principle. He claimed that in the aromatic compounds the linkage between two carbons is stronger than that between a carbon and hydrogen; in the aliphatic compounds the opposite is true. Haber's study was one of the first investigations of the now very important cracking process used in the oil industry. Thermal decomposition or pyrolysis forms a major part of the process of oil cracking.

Haber also studied other fuels during his tenure as assistant, making advances in the methods of coal analysis and probing the nature of the spent gas from gas engines.

At the end of his first two years at Karlsruhe he was ready to present himself as a prospective member of the regular faculty, although the usual period of apprenticeship was six to eight semesters rather than four. An assistant had nothing but prospects for advancement; a *Privatdocent* was a member of the faculty.

The *Privatdocent* received no pay, but the title signified a permit to lecture to students with student fees as compensation. Other professorial posts meant, in addition to a basic salary, the privilege of sharing tuition fees with school authorities. Thus, if a professor was popular and had many students, his compensation was large. Sometimes a benevolent and liberal professor who lectured to a number of students would give his assistants a portion of his earnings, but there was no definite rule about this, not even in chemistry where assistants did much of the laboratory work.

Haber submitted the usual thesis. All the data and results of his first study were collected into one volume entitled, *Experimental Studies on the Decomposition and Combustion of Hydrocarbons*. The book was published in 1896 by the firm of R. Oldenburg in Munich. Critics of the time received the volume cordially. The reviewer for the recently founded *Zeitschrift für Elektrochemie* called it a "worthwhile book" and recommended it to "those who are entrusted with the utilization of our fuels."

Haber was accepted into the regular faculty, and thus arrived at one station on the way to an academic goal. He could now relax. His first two years at Karlsruhe, however, had not been all work; he had enjoyed much friendship and camaraderie.

August Marx, teacher of Greek and Latin at a Karlsruhe

21

high school, was a close companion. Haber nicknamed him Karl August, after the patron of Goethe, the Grand Duke of Saxe-Weimar. Together Marx and Haber went sightseeing, mountain climbing, and dining. Through the association, Haber came to know Greek and Latin better; Marx gradually learned more science. Once when they were in Switzerland, Marx wanted to see an old Roman church while Haber preferred dinner, so they separated with the understanding that Haber would hold their dinner until his friend returned. Marx arrived to find both dinners gone by way of Haber's appetite. Knowing that Haber disliked the heavy, undigestible food popular in South Germany, his friend once sent him a large platter of it, accompanied by a jesting verse. Haber declined the present, adding more digestible delicacies before returning it to Marx.

Other friends at Karlsruhe were a group of scientists, artists, writers, and educators. Fritz Lasch and Hans Steude were his friends; so were Dauber and Hausrath, instructors at the high school, the painter Count Kalckreuth, the architect Sauer, and certain of Haber's colleagues, including Max Mayer, also an assistant to Bunte, and Hans Luggin. Their pleasure was fellowship and the association of kindred spirits. Their activities encompassed Black Forest excursions on Sunday, eating together, discussions and story telling, flippant remarks and humor, arguments and small talk. They called themselves *Mitglied der Tischgesellschaft*— members in fellowship at the table—the M.I.T., and adopted as their motto, "At this table it is permissible to lie a little bit." The young men were just getting started in their careers, and they bolstered their egos with tall tales.

Haber developed his storytelling ability with the M.I.T. He became an adept raconteur and rationalized his exaggerations with the statement, "A story cannot be entirely true and good at the same time." Many of his tales amply illustrate this maxim, particularly one describing his success in the academic world.

One very warm summer day he went hiking in the Swiss mountains. After a jaunt of eight hours, searching for drinking water, he came to a very small, seemingly uninhabited place. Water was not to be found, and he was very thirsty. Finally, he saw a well surrounded by a low wall. He immediately immersed his entire head. At almost the same time and unnoticed by him, a bull had done likewise; neither paid much attention to the other. But when they withdrew from the water, they found their heads had been interchanged. Fritz Haber had a bull's head and prospered as a professor from that eventful day.

✠

3. First Glimmers of Success

✠

Hans Luggin was the son of a well-to-do Austrian merchant. He had studied with Wilhelm Ostwald's friend, the Swedish scientist Svante Arrhenius. Arrhenius had boldly proclaimed that inorganic molecules immersed in water dissociated into electrically charged parts, ions, and Ostwald was one of the few who had championed his findings. Arrhenius became famous for his theory of electrolytic dissociation, but some of the other scientific ideas he advanced came close to science fiction. He was interested in the gold content of the oceans and the origin of life on other planets. Arrhenius and his pupils were, nevertheless, in the forefront of physical chemistry.

Luggin vitally influenced and directed Haber scientifically. He inspired, encouraged, and instructed. Through informal conversation, he introduced Haber to chemistry that had been unknown to him. Haber had the benefit of friendly guidance, individual tutoring, and private discussions. When Luggin died in 1899, Haber wrote a paper on teaching in commemoration of this friend to whom he felt indebted. Luggin had introduced Haber to physical chemistry.

Haber was, as he would often say later, as nearly as possible a self-made man of science. He was in the same self-taught category as such great achievers in science as Blaise

Pascal, Benjamin Franklin, Michael Faraday, and Enrico Fermi. Haber had never been fully satisfied with formal courses at Berlin, Heidelberg, Charlottenburg, or Zurich. But at Karlsruhe, a new interest was awakened. He was enthusiastic enough to study for many months until one or two o'clock in the morning. He soon mastered the principles of the rapidly growing area of knowledge combining physics and chemistry.

He started research in this new realm by first studying the effect of an electric current upon the chemical nitrobenzene, oil of mirbane, a yellowish liquid having a strong odor of oil of bitter almonds. He investigated the electrochemical reduction of nitrobenzene.

Reduction and its necessary counterpart oxidation involve a basic constituent of all earthly matter, the electron. A chemical reaction is an oxidation-reduction reaction whenever electrons are transferred or displaced. This action can come through the direct contact of materials or can be produced with a little heat; results can be good, too, when an electric current, a flow of electrons, gives the unseen, indirectly sensed, negatively charged particles to an acceptor. In the case of nitrobenzene, it is the object of benevolence for the philanthropic electric current.

Previous investigators of the electrochemical reduction of nitrobenzene had done little to isolate relevant factors. Many different products had been detected, but general rules had not been found. With the aid of apparatus specially devised by Luggin, Haber established the importance of the force of the electric current at its junction, the electrode, with the chemical. He showed that the nature of the material produced was governed by this factor.

He did other original work in electrochemistry. He studied the action of an electric current on hydrochloric acid. With his friend Georg Bredig he observed and reported on the pulverization of metal electrodes. He formulated a mechanism having to do with the action of oxygen with and without the presence of water. He proposed an equation to calculate the force of oxidation-reduction changes.

In 1898, Haber published his *Outline of Technical Electrochemistry on a Theoretical Basis*. The book was an effective union of the technical and the theoretical. It was not a justification of one at the expense of the other, but rather pointed out the correlation between them. In arguments for the interdependency of theory and practice, Haber was almost alone. He emphasized the value of co-operation in that all his successful work showed a remarkable union of theory and application.

Haber's association with an engineering school was, in a sense, a tribute to this same belief. Universities attempted to hold themselves aloof from institutes of technology. Professors believed acceptance of a position at a *Technische Hochschule* to be a lowering of rank. Haber saw no point in avoiding a technical school, with its supposed lack of the usual culture and refinement found on a university campus. It did mean an opportunity to apply science, to use the knowledge and methods uncovered since the Renaissance. He believed in such utilitarianism, in studying science for another end as well as for itself. He said, "It is not enough to seek and to know; we must also apply."

Haber's book received a lukewarm welcome in the organ of the German Electrochemical Society. "The attempt of the author," wrote the reviewer, "to teach electrochemistry through the medium of technology is very sympathetically received . . . and the experiment is acknowledged to be in general successful. . . . The author . . . has not yet had the opportunity to lead a great electrical works. The reviewer cannot agree with all the ideas, especially those . . . diverging from all bases of accepted belief." On page 195 was an equation which "as far as the reviewer knows . . . is until now only put together by *Herr* Haber alone." A better reception was given to the book by the official organ of the gas and water chemists, of which Hans Bunte was editor. It recommended the volume to its readers, although the book was not directly concerned with gas or water chemistry. Haber had published some of his research results in their *Journal für Gasbeleuchtung und Wasserversorgung;* he had addressed members of a section of their society at Heilbronn on August 1, 1897.

In Ostwald's laboratory at Leipzig, the students, many of whom became recognized leaders in physical chemistry, read the book avidly. Some called Haber "a very clever man." The wealth of data in the book prompted Ostwald to remark, "It seems as though he empties a large pail of facts over our heads."

The book was an important reason for his promotion to associate professor. Beginning his career as an organic chemist, he now made his way in electro and physical chemistry. He became more prominent at the meetings of the German Electrochemical Society. At the fifth annual convention in Leipzig, April 14 and 15, 1898, he spoke about the gradual reduction of nitrobenzene. At the eighth meeting, in Freiburg, April 17–20, 1901, he was a well-known attendant. He and several others joined in endorsing Ostwald's suggestion that the organization change its name to the Bunsen Society. It was a fitting tribute that was later adopted; in 1841, Robert Bunsen's battery had marked a new era in the economical production of electricity.

Haber met many friendly colleagues at the meetings.

Max Bodenstein, Gerhard Just, and Georg Bredig came from Leipzig; his old friend Paul Askenasy came from Vienna; and Richard Abegg, his former classmate, traveled from Breslau. At the Freiburg convention, one of Abegg's students, Fräulein Dr. Clara Immerwahr, was present. Her doctoral dissertation, "On the Solubility of Metal Precipitates," had been published in the organ of the society; she had been the first woman to receive a doctorate in chemistry from the University of Breslau. But, more important, Clara Immerwahr was an old love, dating back to Haber's teens.

She was a native of Breslau. Her family had resided in the area for several generations. Her grandfather had been a prosperous merchant; he had been well enough established to sell Oriental rugs to the Emperor; he went to Paris on buying trips in his own coach. Her father, Dr. Philip Immerwahr, a university graduate, managed a sugar refinery and owned a large farm in Silesia on which Clara had been born.

Clara Immerwahr, fifteen years old, met Fritz Haber, eighteen, at dancing school. The attraction was immediate for Haber; he proposed marriage almost as soon as he knew her and she responded.

The young couple planned and dreamed; they had all the pleasures, the beautiful oneness, of courtship and companionship. Lovers, they believed themselves ordained by fate for union. They thought no one else could be involved in their strong bond of affection, in their private world of bliss and expectation. But the parents intervened. Guiders of the young, supposed authorities in the good life for their children, they opposed the marriage. Moreover, they would not allow it. Custom called for marriage when the man was established and successful, when the age of twenty was in the remote past. There would be no parasitic dependence upon the money of parents.

When Fritz Haber was finished with his schooling, he did not have means to support a wife. Nonetheless, he continued to see small, slender, fair-haired Clara. At Christmas they exchanged gifts; once she sent him sugar candy with almonds. His economic future appeared brighter after he became associated with his father in business; at last they became engaged. The engagement was broken soon after the chloride of lime debacle and his return to the academic world. Perhaps, also, he decided against a quiet, unassuming woman who lisped. She, too, was a young woman with ideas—one could have been to avoid being a housewife. Yet she was in love with him; she studied chemistry in order to be nearer to him.

With the passage of time neither Fritz Haber nor Clara Immerwahr knew another romantic love. Yet they had seen very little of each other since breaking their engagement. They were brought together again by his first cousin. Clara and the daughter of Fritz Haber's favorite uncle, Hermann, were good friends; the girls had been classmates in the study of French and Italian languages, literature, and the humanities.

He was thirty-three years old; she was thirty. Since their happy days of youth, both had acquired other interests, new points of view, and new habits; their love had been tempered by worldly experience and negation. But it was still strong. A Breslau newspaper noted one day during the summer of 1901 that Fräulein Dr. Immerwahr would soon become Frau Professor Haber. Fritz and Clara were married in the summer of 1901, three months after the convention in Freiburg.

They rented the first floor of a lawyer's villa, near the Karlsruhe woods and about a ten-minute walk from the school. The attorney occupied the second floor. Minus the money for a full-time servant, Mrs. Haber did the necessary household chores.

She continued scientific work for some months. She was interested in it and ambitious for accomplishments in the field. Later she lectured about the chemistry of home economics. But with the birth of a son and increasing home obligations, she retired from science. However, in 1911 she translated two important articles, first published in England and made available in Germany by the Bunsen Society.

The almost complete abandonment of her laboratory training was one reason for her growing dissatisfaction. It was a kind of frustration; she was too much educated to be only a housewife. The difficult birth of her child changed her, too. Then marriage, she found, was not the Elysian paradise.

Fritz Haber was not a perfect husband nor a perfect lover. His actions, as far as she was concerned, showed an inexcusable absent-mindedness. One day in the summer of 1901, the two, then engaged, planned a train and hiking trip. He entered the railroad station to purchase the tickets while his fiancée waited outside. She was patient too long; when she finally went into the building, he was not in sight. Her inquiries at the ticket window brought to her dismay the answer that a man of Haber's description had taken the train to Karlsruhe a moment ago. He had forgotten, inadvertently or not, his waiting bride-to-be. He showed a frequent lack of consideration. Many times he failed to come home for dinner at the regular time. This made Mrs. Haber frantic—as did his habit of appearing at eleven or twelve o'clock at night with several friends to ask for supper for all. Then, too, he began to scold her when she visited him at school. He would send her out of the room with, "Can't you see I'm busy?" Only infrequently did he welcome her.

While still somewhat active in science, she was alert in reaction and thought. Returning home one evening, she was accosted by a thug. He seized her purse and ran swiftly into the adjacent woods. Outraged, Mrs. Haber pursued him. She pretended to have a gun and demanded the return of her purse. She retrieved her bag and went on her way. The thought of danger, of a dark forest, and of physical harm had been absent in her quick thinking. However, as the housewife role became her sole one, she became less spirited and spontaneous, and perhaps lost her former brilliance. Allowing herself to become stout, untidy, and unattractive, she retained only a dutiful interest in her husband and his work. Where once similar backgrounds and similar interests had fostered deep attachment, a lethargic tolerance developed, and the marriage slowly began to disintegrate.

At the Würzburg convention of the Bunsen Society in 1902, Fritz Haber was selected to observe the technical and educational progress of the United States. After being a member but five years, he was sent as an expert to study and to report. Professor Jacobus Hendricus van't Hoff, an early colleague of Ostwald's, donated two thousand marks for the study.

Haber's former teacher, Otto N. Witt, professor of chemical technology at Charlottenburg *Technische Hochschule*, had visited the 1893 World's Columbian Exposition in Chicago. Witt observed, "The few coal-tar dye factories in America are small and unimportant and are not able to supply more than a very small fraction of the domestic demand for these products. The major portion of these products will continue to be imported from Europe, principally from Germany." In 1901, Hans Bunte had visited Boston and other cities in eastern United States. At last Haber was to be among many Germans traveling, observing, and learning.

Fritz Haber was not the first member of his family to cross the Atlantic. Another had sought and won a fortune in America. His father's oldest brother, Edward, had found wealth in Central America, only to lose it at Monte Carlo. The uncle had then made a second fortune in the New World, with which he returned to Hamburg in 1900 to retire.

Fritz Haber's sixteen-week itinerary in the United States, late spring until early autumn, 1902, extended from New York to California. (Clara Haber was pregnant and did not accompany her husband; in June, 1902, a son, Hermann, was born.) Haber visited eleven widely scattered universities and representative factories among the 2,200 chemical plants then in the country. Like many other visitors, he marveled at the unparalleled activity in New York harbor, California sunshine, and what he called "cities of eternal summer" in the West. He was greatly impressed by the people; he admired their enterprise, independence, courage, and national pride.

He found the training for chemists to be superficial and practical, and American educators agreed with him. He brought back to Germany and translated with Dr. M. Stoecker Professor Alexander Smith's *Laboratory Outline of General Chemistry*. This book was translated also into Russian and Italian, besides having six American editions.

Haber described, in his report, the processes of chemical manufacturing in detail. Whenever substantiated facts were not available, he made reasonable assumptions. The Pittsburgh Reduction Company refused to disclose the exact amount of power it used. An American chemist guessed, after considering known factors, the amount to be 10,500 horsepower. Haber postulated 15,500 horsepower "as nearer the truth."

The editors of *Electrochemical Industry* wrote that he, as a "distinguished representative of the modern German scientific school of electrochemistry and physical chemistry," made a report that was "one of the ablest and most complete papers which have been published on this subject, and is extremely suggestive on account of many remarks of a critical and general nature."

Haber was well received in the United States. American scientists were friendly hosts, and he spent many nights in their homes; for instance, he was the overnight guest of a dean of American chemists, Wilder D. Bancroft, of Cornell University at Ithaca, New York. He was a special guest of the five-month-old American Electrochemical Society when it met for the second time, September, 1902, at Niagara Falls. Ninety per cent of the fourteen electrochemical works in the United States were at the Falls. Fritz Haber favorably impressed the two hundred delegates attending the sessions. Many years later, one recalled him as a "bright, physically and mentally alert young man whose presence . . . was appreciated by all. He added materially to the success of our gathering." In 1904, two years after the meeting, *Electrochemical Industry* called the attention of the "numerous friends" of Dr. Fritz Haber to his planning of the German exhibits in the chemical and apparatus industries section at the St. Louis Exposition. (This was the grand spectacle to celebrate the hundredth anniversary of the Louisiana Purchase.)

In November, 1902, Haber returned to a prosperous and growing Germany. The country was on the surge of industrial expansion. Urban population grew seven times as rapidly as did the rural. From 1875 to 1895 steel production jumped from thirty-five thousand to two and one-half million tons. In 1902, the number of chemical factories was more than ten thousand, twice as many as in 1895. The output of sulfuric acid and alkalies rose eight times between 1870 and 1900; that of dyestuffs rose four times.

Citizens in this flourishing Germany were interested in another thriving country. Haber reported his observations of the United States to many groups. For the Bunsen Society, his lecture was held in Hofmann Haus, Berlin; before Karlsruhe engineers, he showed photographs of American factories; for engineering societies in the major cities of Germany, he spoke about "The Role of Electrochemistry in Modern Technology."

His students were also treated to comments on America. In classroom and laboratory, they heard his ideas. His duties at Karlsruhe comprised the teaching of dyestuff chemistry, the chemistry of textiles for junior-year students, and introductory portions of electrochemistry. Later, gas chemistry became his responsibility, and he began to guide fourth-year research students.

The problems he assigned and directed were theoretical and practical. He undertook to know more about the iron plates used in the printing of bank notes—a study usually done in a commercial laboratory. He investigated the corrosion of underground gas and water pipes due to stray currents emitted from the direct current then operating streetcars. His first patent was for a technique of staining cotton and other plant fibers with chromium. He was involved with theory. He was interested in passivity, the apparent lack of behavior of a metal, usually iron. He worked on the concentration of constituents in current-conducting solutions. He gave an explanation for the ability of some solid chemical compounds to be passageways for electricity.

Along with many other scientists at the turn of the century, he was interested in fuel cells—arrangements of chemicals in which electric current is produced through the action of atmospheric oxygen on carbon or carbon dioxide. Fuel cells have both theoretical and practical importance. From the latter point of view, they increase the efficiency of obtaining energy from coal. When energy is obtained from burning—when coal, coke, or wood is set on fire—less than 25 per cent of the total amount of heat energy liberated by the combustion is capable of being used. The greater percentage is lost. Likewise the gas engine uses about the same amount of the available energy of its fuel. One possible way of making the conversion of energy more efficient is to change the energy of combustion directly into electricity without the intermediate production of heat. This means electrochemically combining the fuel and atmospheric oxygen. A fuel cell thus has revolutionary significance. To obtain electricity directly from coal, without in-between stages, would be as important an accomplishment as was the invention of the steam engine or the release of nuclear energy. A complete success would eliminate the smoke problem and save time, energy, money, and labor. Haber made a striking discovery in a cell where carbon and iron were immersed in melted sodium hydroxide. He showed that the iron behaved as though a film of active oxygen surrounded the metal.

With the passage of time, electrochemistry became one of Haber's main interests. The subject was popular and practical; many believed a vast new industry would be one result of combining the subjects of electricity and chemistry. In 1900, a professorship of physical and electrochemistry was founded at Karlsruhe. In April, 1901, plans were drawn for a building to house an institute for physical chemistry and

35

electrochemistry. By December, 1903, the construction was nearing an end.

Max Le Blanc, associated with the *Chemische Fabrik Griesheim-Elektron,* was chosen to direct the institute. In the spring of 1901, the works of this organization at Griesheim, near Frankfurt, burned almost to the ground. The resulting lull in production had provided a good opportunity for the company to secure an academic post for Le Blanc. He was a tall, stiff East Prussian with a handle-bar mustache. His gait and bearing prompted the description, "He walks parallel to himself." He was acknowledged to have executive and diplomatic abilities as well as a talented wife. He had been an assistant to Ostwald at Leipzig. He was an advisory editor of the *Zeitschrift für Elektrochemie.* His textbook on electrochemistry had been so clearly written that for many years it was found in every good library.

Le Blanc found a challenging young scientist in Haber, one who would bluntly point out errors and comment without considering feelings. Others would talk among themselves, privately discussing merits and demerits. Haber could never explain to his friends, who cautioned him, why he persisted in publicly evaluating Le Blanc, why he analyzed with such brilliance and frankness the work of his superior.

Haber was respected for his ability as a critic. If someone made but one error, gave one false interpretation, said one sentence which was not very clear, Haber called attention to the flaw. He was a spontaneous condemner of falsity without regard for propriety. Once a student made a small mistake when writing an equation on the blackboard; Haber was vehement in his denunciation. Indeed, at the start of his career he failed a large percentage of his students.

He seemed not to know or was not eager to use the technique of flattery to gain his ends. Repeatedly he had asked Bunte to order new furniture for his laboratory. Consistently, Bunte had refused. Haber confided in a colleague, who showed him how to obtain the furniture by using a little tact. He called on Bunte and during the visit suggested that a man in Bunte's position, who received important visitors in his office, needed newer and finer furnishings. Bunte was pleased, but perplexed about the disposal of his old furniture. "What shall I do with it?" he asked. "Oh, give it to Haber; he needs it," the colleague suggested. Thus Haber became heir to Bunte's serviceable discards.

In 1905, Fritz Haber's *Thermodynamics of Technical Gas Reactions* was published. The book was dedicated to his wife for "her silent co-operation." She had aided, mainly in silence, in the details of verifying and computing data. Both had worked at the book in the library of their apartment at two different desks. His students, too, had helped. He had read the manuscript notes to his advanced classes as he had fashioned the material into a book. Likewise his industrial friends had been of value. With the collaboration of the Carl Zeiss Optical Works at Jena, whose owner he had sponsored for membership to the Bunsen Society, Haber devised an instrument for industrial gas analysis.

He was most proud of his third book. It was translated into English soon after publication. Haber co-operated in this, giving permission provided a good publisher were found, checking the translation, and even adding some new material. He thought the English version was excellent. Only once he adversely criticized—when the translator missed the point of a geological analogy Haber had used.

In 1906, after the book had been circulated and read, Haber was named a full professor at Karlsruhe as well as the director of the Electrochemistry Institute. Le Blanc had been invited to Leipzig to succeed Ostwald.

Haber had been chosen to investigate American electrochemistry; yet when an institute devoted to this specialty had been founded at Karlsruhe he had not been appointed director. His failure to obtain the post at first can be attributed to the desire of the school authorities for an outside scientist with more extensive experience in industry, as well as to Le Blanc's influential friends. Perhaps anti-Semitism was also a factor, even in the early 1900's.

In 1903, Haber had applied for a vacant professorship at Stuttgart. He was a third choice, with two less distinguished, less accomplished, and less talented scientists being given preference. Jewish ancestry could have been the reason he was not selected. Disillusioned, Haber was consoled by friends. He was assured that the time would come when he would be immensely successful.

He became a Protestant to insure this prophecy. Poet Heinrich Heine had called such conversions obtaining "a passport into European culture." The passport was often tainted, looked upon askance, classified separately, and tolerated rather than appreciated. Few of the baptisms grew out of religious or philosophical convictions.

Haber had never been a real adherent to the Jewish faith. He had not been reared as a Jew. His stepmother, once ambitious to be a concert pianist, was thoroughly assimilated. Her father had not observed Jewish festivals and had both Jewish and Christian friends. He had been an 1848 revolutionist who believed himself a staunch German. In her uncle's house in Thorn, Poland, she had danced at parties with Christian army officers. Siegfried Haber had never insisted on Jewish customs in his home. He, as well as his brother and two sisters, had received an education at the

Gymnasium in Brieg, a small town one hour by railroad from Breslau.

Siegfried's father, Jacob, had been a prosperous wool merchant. In his early thirties, he had been stricken with cholera and had been buried in Brody, Poland. (During World War I his grandson Fritz Haber visited the grave.) The widow, formerly Carolina Friedlander, and her six children were supported by Jacob's brother, Julius. Although Julius had ten children of his own, his income had been sufficient to care for two families. The brothers had been partners in business; Jacob had traveled; Julius had been responsible for office affairs.

Fritz Haber's great grandfather, the father of Jacob, Julius, and another son whose name is unknown, had been Pinkus Seelig Haber, a Jewish merchant of Silesia. He could have been the Zeleg Haber mentioned in a Karlsbad newspaper during the early 1800's. He may have been "the well-known merchant of Breslau" who had happened to visit the spa while the great German poet and dramatist Goethe was resting at the resort. There is a possibility, too, that he is the Haber who had served as a regimental surgeon with the Prussian Army during the Napoleonic wars.

During the nineteenth century many Jews in all countries were dissociating themselves from their more religious brethren. German Jewry, in general, tended to be more German and less Jewish. In contrast to the Jews in Russia, German Jews were privileged citizens in an expanding country. Their appreciation for this condition was reflected in the allegiance which they gave to Germany, their contributions to the welfare of the land, and their attempts to break away entirely from less fortunate European Jewry. The nineteenth century, furthermore, was considered a new age in the social and cultural development of man. People believed

they were living in an enlightened period and that the cruel-
ties of former centuries were excluded then and for the
future. Those hopeful ones who looked for the disappear-
ance of anti-Semitism gave specious attention, for example,
to Russian and Polish pogroms.

Fritz Haber had never been intensely interested in Jewish
problems, although as a young man he had been too ready to
assign many a failure, defeat, or misfortune to anti-Semitism. It was an easy and common rationalization even
among the assimilated. He and many other German Jews
believed anti-Semitism could be amelioriated by conversion.
The vogue was Christianity. The belief was adjustment.
As he said, there was no use being in the "herring belt" all
his life. Talented and industrious Jews were becoming successful. There was no need to be acutely aware of minor
discriminations; they were practiced against other groups
too. Roman Catholics were not very well liked in Prussia
nor Protestants in Bavaria and Austria. In the United States,
Fritz Haber met a type of anti-Semitism unknown to him
in Germany, and he was shocked. In 1902, an American
Jewish friend took him to Atlantic City for a weekend.
As they approached their hotel, Haber saw a sign in front
of the building marked, "No Jews." He hesitated and turned
to his friend, "I guess we are not wanted here." The friend
answered, "That sign is not meant for our kind of Jew."

Siegfried Haber was a capable businessman and later a
city alderman, although he never became a Christian. His
brother Julius probably abdicated Judaism in order to become a Supreme Court judge. In Breslau, a prominent German Jewish banker, but no relation, Solomon von Haber,
had never been baptized. But the banker's son moved to
Karlsruhe and, like Fritz Haber, became a Protestant. Haber's friend August Marx remained Jewish. He was the first

of his faith to become a high school principal in Gerlach-sheim, a town near Karlsruhe. Many of Haber's research students were Jewish, and some found baptism helpful on the road to success.

✠

4. The Ammonia Synthesis

✠

AT THE BEGINNING of the twentieth century, Sir William Crookes, a prominent English scientist, warned mankind of approaching starvation. His forecast was based upon a growing world scarcity of fertilizer containing nitrogen. The element is one of those not always available in sufficient quantities in soil, but essential for proper plant growth. (Nitrogen is also necessary for war purposes; it is in every known explosive except the atomic and hydrogen bombs.)

Bacteria can be a source for fertilizer nitrogen; some species serve as media for the passage of nitrogen from the air to the deficient earth, but they feed on vital soil sugar or function only when plants of the pea family are present. Coal can be decomposed to yield its approximately 1 per cent of nitrogen. Saltpeter can be laboriously made from manure. But taken together these methods were and are incapable of supplying the world demand. The beds of nitrates in Chile were a much richer source of supply. In 1900, Chile provided two-thirds of the fertilizer nitrogen used around the world, and in 1913, Germany took about one-third of the total Chilean production. The rate of consumption was so great that the natural nitrate deposits in South America were becoming exhausted, and it was necessary to find a new source of nitrogen.

Nitrogen is plentiful in the atmosphere. Almost 80 per cent of every cubic foot of air is nitrogen; above every square yard of the earth's surface is about seven tons of the gaseous element. Extraction from the air seemed to be the obvious solution to the nitrogen shortage, and scientists recognized this fact. By 1915 more than three thousand articles about obtaining nitrogen from the air had been published. Yet all the means devised to fix or combine nitrogen of the air were faulty. Either the installation cost was exorbitant, the upkeep and repair of installations expensive, the process inefficient, raw materials not abundant, or the procedure only suitable where water power was plentiful. In 1913, Chile still supplied three-fifths of the nitrogen used.

One method of fixing nitrogen is based upon the ability of nitrogen to attach itself to calcium carbide at a high temperature. After a reaction lasting one or two days, a black powder, cyanamide, results; this material produces skin inflammations when handled too frequently. Although sometimes used directly as a fertilizer it can be changed into a more suitable form; by adding water to it a compound, dicyanamide, is formed that is used to lower the temperature of explosions.

The cyanide process is another nitrogen-fixation scheme. Here sodium carbonate, carbon, and iron are mixed and heated in a stream of nitrogen. Sodium cyanide forms in the midst of unchanged iron. However, this compound is not usable in fertilizers or explosives; it is employed in gold refining and electroplating. Air and steam at high temperature can react with sodium cyanide to form ammonia and soda. Ammonia is removed and processed into fertilizers and the soda can be used again.

The arc process is one of the first nitrogen-fixation methods to be developed. It is so named because a combination of nitrogen and oxygen takes place in an electric arc. The formed nitric oxide is converted into nitric acid through treatment with water and oxygen; the acid can be used by the explosives industry. To produce nitrogen suitable for fertilizer, the acid is mixed with lime to make nitrate of lime.

In 1902 two American chemists built an arc process factory, the Atmospheric Products Company, at Niagara Falls. Fritz Haber visited the establishment and reported its worth. "In spite of the importance of this undertaking," he wrote, "I cannot deny that its status of development has disappointed me somewhat after the description which I had read in the papers. I expected to find an industrial operation and I found an experimental apparatus; true, it is of very great interest, but as far as I can see it is not possible to judge with safety what the commercial result will be."

Mr. Charles S. Bradley, president of the Atmospheric Products Company, agreed that Haber's criticism of the process was largely correct, but noted that the criticism was of a kind which tended "to injure the commercial development." There was a hint of bitterness.

Haber replied, "I have never, in anything I have published, had such a thought, and I do not see how such construction can be placed upon my impartial remarks about the Atmospheric Products Company. I very highly appreciate the great success of this company in the production of nitrous fumes from the air, and I have emphasized my admiration for their work in my report. The result of the work of the company in transforming nitrous fumes into strong nitric acid is, however, still unknown to me; but should Mr. Bradley convince me of his success in this respect, none will be more glad than myself to acknowledge the very high merit of the commercial value of the process."

A few years after his American visit, Haber investigated

more closely the formation of nitric oxide. He had one student combine gases with compressed oxygen; high temperatures were obtained along with richer yields of nitrous oxide. He had another student pass a mixture of oxygen and nitrogen through an alternating current device. At one time, he had the apparently comic situation of a very tall Russian and two small Japanese students working on the arc process.

Norwegian as well as other German scientists had tried with a modicum of success to combine nitrogen and oxygen more efficiently. They used such stratagems as flat disks and elongated circular arcs. Haber thought he would be even more fortunate. In July, 1907, German and British patents were granted him for the "production of compounds of nitrogen and oxygen from atmospheric air, or other mixtures of nitrogen and oxygen by subjecting such air or mixture to the action of an electric arc." A very large organization, the *Badische Anilin und Soda Fabrik,* was much interested in this work. They were ready to encourage its development and buy his patents. It seemed to be a real achievement. But Haber's other accomplishment in nitrogen fixation overshadowed the arc process improvement.

In 1904, the Margulies brothers of Vienna, whom he sponsored for membership to the Bunsen Society in 1907, asked him to study the formation of ammonia from the elements. The two scientists who owned the company could not have been too hopeful of obtaining ammonia from the combination of nitrogen and hydrogen. Established investigators had reported that the combination of the elements could barely be detected.

Haber approached this seemingly insoluble problem with energy and enthusiasm. He tried several methods of obtaining ammonia. One short-lived experiment involved the reaction between calcium nitride and hydrogen at high

45

temperatures. When only traces of ammonia resulted, he concentrated on various conditions for the direct union of the elements. He and student Gabriel van Oordt, using dry gases, found very little ammonia formation at a temperature as high as one thousand degrees centigrade; at best, about one-hundreth of 1 per cent of the desired product was available. More heat and speed-up agents, catalysts, did not raise the amount appreciably. He and another student fed nitrogen and hydrogen mixtures into heavy quartz tubes heated in an electric stove. The minute amount of product formed necessitated searching for sensitive ammonia indicators. The practically negligible amount of ammonia formed in all his experiments did not satisfy anyone concerned. It was certainly not large enough to capture the interest of even far-sighted industrialists. Financial support from the Margulies brothers stopped.

Professor Walther Nernst, physical chemist at the University of Berlin, examined Haber's reports of his work. Nernst was collecting data to test his heat theorem. According to it, Haber's results were erroneous. Nernst and his co-workers set out to establish the correct figures. With this consideration they also intended to increase the amount of ammonia formed.

An analysis of the equation indicated the greater production goal. The synthesis is symbolized

$$N_2 + 3H_2 \rightleftarrows 2NH_3 + \text{heat energy.}$$

Many facts are incorporated in this equation: The symbols for nitrogen, hydrogen and ammonia; each molecule of elementary gas has two atoms; the molecules of the gas ammonia have one nitrogen atom combined with three hydrogen atoms; one volume or molecule of nitrogen combines with three volumes or molecules of hydrogen to yield two volumes or molecules of ammonia; the number of atoms of any one kind are the same before and after the process—only their arrangement and connections change; the amount of raw material, reactants or reagents, equals in weight the amount of product; heat is emitted in the synthesis; the formation of ammonia proceeds along with its simultaneous decomposition. When the two processes, union and disruption of ammonia, are equal in speed, the condition of chemical equilibrium is attained. This stable state can come at any temperature.

Any chemical equilibrium reacts to many forces and the result in each case conforms to the principle of least action. This common sense idea "predicts" that a stone lying on top of a hill—in mechanical equilibrium—will roll down if pushed; that an automobile at rest—in mechanical equilibrium—will move if started; that water will flow if a closed faucet is opened. Nature takes the path of least effort in mechanical or chemical equilibria. In mechanical equilibria, objects are at rest; in chemical equilibria, molecules of reagent are continually forming molecules of product and the reverse is taking place at an equal rate. Forces that can upset mechanical equilibria are easily visualized; forces that upset chemical equilibria are those affecting the speed of reaction, such as temperature and concentration.

When the gases nitrogen, hydrogen, and ammonia are in chemical equilibrium, changes in concentration can affect the situation. Should more nitrogen be added to this system, its easiest way out is to absorb the increase by using the added nitrogen. The rate of formation of ammonia is speeded, and a new equilibrium is finally reached with a greater concentration of ammonia. Likewise, an addition of hydrogen to the equilibrium system steps up the amount of product formed per unit time and a new equilibrium

47

state with a greater percentage of ammonia is obtained. Of course, adding amounts of both reagents gives a better result than adding amounts of only one reagent. In any event, large quantities of hydrogen and nitrogen remain uncombined regardless of the conditions.

Temperature changes are another avenue for modifying an equilibrium condition to obtain a more favorable one. The equation for the ammonia synthesis indicates that heat is produced; it is an exothermic reaction. Consequently removing that heat or cooling the equilibrium vessel should increase the ammonia production. It is possible to consider heat energy as an item added to make ammonia decompose more rapidly or subtracted to make the ammonia synthesize more speedily, just as nitrogen or hydrogen is added to make for more concentration and availability of combination. Too low a temperature has disadvantages. The reactants become stolid; they need some heat energy to become active and begin a union. Too high a temperature must also be avoided. The system of gases reacts to high heat with a greater break-up of ammonia; the more heat applied, the more decomposition. The actual temperature used must be a compromise between the desideratum of speed and of yield. At a very high temperature, the rate of association is good, but the ammonia proceeds to decompose. At a very low temperature the speed of formation is less, yet the product thrives on the condition. Thus a moderate temperature must be used.

The equilibrium condition at any temperature can be obtained more rapidly with the use of catalysts. These are chemicals that make speedier both forward and backward reactions in an equilibrium. They do so without in any way being modified themselves. Most catalysts afford a surface for efficient chemical change and are for this reason speed-up agents; others form more easily made intermediates that quickly decompose.

Since the ammonia equilibrium is concerned with gases, pressure changes at a constant temperature can also affect the concentration and thus the equilibrium point. The equation indicates that four volumes of reagent become two volumes of products; an increase in pressure favors an equilibrium point where more product is formed because two spaces can be better contained by pressure than can four spaces. Haber was familiar with Le Châtelier's law dealing with the equilibrium of a system when subjected to stress. In 1901, French chemist Henry Le Châtelier synthesized ammonia with the help of extra pressure. Although his final result was a disastrous explosion, he was granted a French patent that year and the application of the principle of least action to chemical equilibria is now called Châtelier's theorem. So Nernst and Haber had a foundation on which to build.

Nernst and his students conducted ammonia synthesis experiments with pressures from fifty to seventy-five times as high as is produced by the weight of the atmosphere; instead of 14.7 pounds per square inch they used anywhere from 735 to 1,102.5 pounds per square inch on the reaction vessel. They obtained data at variance with Haber's but consistent with Nernst's predictions. Nernst so informed Haber by letter in the autumn of 1906.

Haber was not content to accept the results of the influential and respected Nernst. Eagerly and cautiously he repeated his experiments. But still his figures were about 50 per cent larger than Nernst's.

At the exciting Hamburg meeting of the Bunsen Society in the summer of 1907, both Nernst and Haber, armed with data and explanations, were present. Both were certain of their own correctness. If Nernst were wrong, his heat theorem would have to be reconsidered and likewise his scientific standing. An error would mean a tumbling reputation for Haber. In 1906, Haber had been criticized for an erroneous report; one of his students had made inaccurate determinations in studying the reaction between oxygen and magnesium chloride. Ideas were not so much a dispute between Nernst and Haber. The conflict involved analytical exactness. Nernst's arguments centered about his experiments with high pressure. These Haber had not tried for a practical reason; the apparatus was too cumbersome. Nernst had the last word at the meeting. He suggested that Haber perform high-pressure experiments. He regretted, too, that the high values were not really true. Otherwise he could think of commercial possibilities.

Haber took Nernst's statements as somewhat of a personal affront. Immediately upon his return to Karlsruhe he focused his attention on the ammonia synthesis. It was his intention to have the last word. His collaborator and student was Robert Le Rossignol, an Englishman. Son of a physician on the Isle of Jersey, he had been trained in Sir William Ramsay's laboratory in England. A skillful and ingenious experimenter, he did all of the laboratory and some of the machine shop work. The talented mechanic Kirchenbauer was responsible for most of the latter. Working with higher pressures, Haber and Le Rossignol confirmed Haber's earliest values. This gave him a renewed confidence that had been shaken a little at Hamburg. For a while it seemed that the accepted king of physical chemistry, Nernst, had been dethroned by Haber. But Nernst's heat theorem was not wrong. A fundamental value used in performing calculations with it was shown to be erroneous.

Haber and Le Rossignol went forward to other conquests. They began experiments toward commercial application of the synthesis. According to their results, larger quantities of ammonia could be expected at apparently unattainable conditions. Eight per cent was to be had with a pressure of two hundred atmospheres and a temperature of six hundred degrees centigrade. Such small yields were known to manufacturers but the tremendous heat and force was something new to them. A high pressure process for industry would be a bold innovation. Combining it with as high a temperature as six hundred degrees would also be pioneering. Two materials were necessary: an apparatus to withstand high pressure and a capable catalyst. After an extensive search, Haber found efficient catalysts in uranium and osmium—usable as either metal, alloy, nitride, or carbide. Le Rossignol and Kirchenbauer were very helpful in the quest for an ultra-strong container. Nernst had used porcelain. Haber and his group introduced metal.

Haber interested industry, through his friend and colleague Karl Engler, on the technical and advisory staff of the *Badische Anilin und Soda Fabrik*. The *Badische* Company paid him a twenty-five hundred dollar retainer and promised to purchase further developments. On July 2, 1909, two representatives of the company visited Haber's laboratory. They were Karl Bosch, research engineer, and Alwin Mittasch, chemist and catalysis expert. Haber escorted them to the apparatus, but, as if in defiance of discerning eyes, the system refused to operate. Then a bolt broke while being tightened. After a quick examination, Bosch concluded that the process would not work, and he left Karlsruhe. Mittasch decided to remain awhile and await developments. Later in the day, Mittasch saw the process produce one hundred cubic centimeters of ammonia. This

51

convinced him as well as others who saw a demonstration.

At Haber's request the *Badische* Company made a unique settlement for his patents. Instead of the usual percentage of net sales, he was to receive a flat sum, one *pfennig*, for every kilogram of product sold. He reasoned that when production increased, costs would correspondingly decrease, and prices would be lower. Total sales would have to increase at a rate equal to production cost decreases in order to have a stable royalty income. Whereas a flat sum payment for every kilogram sold would guarantee a stable income no matter how cheap the product became. Haber made his own arrangements with Le Rossignol and Kirchenbauer; the former received a very sizeable percentage of Haber's income.

Haber's ammonia synthesis became the solution to mankind's nitrogen shortage. By 1963, 278 synthetic ammonia plants were in operation and another 43 were under construction throughout the world.

✠

5. Farewell to Karlsruhe

✠

NITROGEN FIXATION was but an episode in the controversy between Nernst and Haber. Since the turn of the century, they had been growing scientific adversaries. The contest between them was for recognition as the number one physical chemist. It became, too, a struggle for the center position in the scientific world.

Walther Nernst was born, four and one-half years before Haber, about twenty miles northeast of the birthplace of Copernicus, at Briesen, West Prussia, now called Wabrzezno, Poland. Like Haber, he greatly enjoyed the classics and literature and once had ambitions to be a poet. He admired Shakespeare, and at one time suggested the term "falstaff" as a unit for amount of liquid flow. In 1897 he developed, patented, and sold, for one million marks, a light source which required less power than the then prevalent carbon filament lamp. Haber had been an investigating emissary to America in 1902; Nernst in 1904. Haber had been anxious to become professor of physical chemistry at Leipzig. Nernst, influential with the Minister of Education, had blocked this appointment. In Haber's *Thermodynamics* book was a statement that more or less became Nernst's heat theorem—the third law of thermodynamics, that Kelvin zero temperature is not attainable. Nernst is said to have begun his lectures on thermodynamics by saying, "The first law of thermodynamics rests on the shoulders of many; the second law on the shoulders of few; the third, on the shoulders of one—mine."

The competitors were keen. Both were intellectual giants, ambitious, talented, and clever. Nernst was the better theorist, but Haber was the better critic. Haber was practical and could appreciate industrial application. Before Haber's achievement, Nernst had asked a prominent manufacturer whether the ammonia synthesis would be feasible; he was told it was impossible, and he dropped the matter.

Nernst was even smaller than Haber's five-foot, five inches, and he had a large head. The appellation by some, "the little Nernst," belied his scientific worth. His conclusions were generally accepted as accurate; he was one of the founders of electrochemistry; he had a seldom duplicated genius for mathematical reasoning. After Nernst's death in 1942, Albert Einstein wrote about him, "He was an original personality. I have never met anyone who resembled him in any essential way. . . . He had a truly amazing scientific instinct combined with a sovereign knowledge of an enormous volume of factual materials, which was always at his command, and with a rare mastery of the experimental methods and tricks in which he excelled."

Nernst was undoubtedly a major instigator of Haber's brilliant accomplishment. Nernst was the first to form ammonia from the elements under pressure. But Copernicus is credited with the heliocentric theory, not Aristarchus of Samos. Galileo is said to be the discoverer of the laws governing falling bodies, not Simon Stevin. So Haber is responsible for the ammonia synthesis; to set the record straight, he is the Columbus of nitrogen fixation.

Publicly, Nernst and Haber were friendly but not friends.

Haber, in private conversation, bitterly criticized Nernst. The latter told his classes that the Haber process was really his. Occasionally both failed to appear at scientific gatherings when each learned the other had been invited. Perhaps such indulgences are the privilege of first-rate scientists who dislike being proved wrong.

In some respects Haber began to outdistance Nernst at the beginning of the twentieth century. Students came to him in preference to his fellow scientist. Silesian-born Friedrich Bergius, a former student of Abegg's in Breslau, spent a year with Nernst and then came to Karlsruhe for further training. When Bergius later applied the high-pressure technique to the action of hydrogen on coal, thus producing oil, he won a Nobel prize. An American en route to Nernst's laboratory heard so much about Haber that he applied at Karlsruhe instead. Haber's laboratory became a goal for young scientists, a center upheld as a haven for the best. The once famous Ostwald Institute, where Max Le Blanc reigned, felt the effect of Haber's popularity. The Leipzig school steadily declined, and Le Blanc queried the Minister of Education about the meaning of his dwindling student body and the Karlsruhe Institute's corresponding jump in fame and enrollment.

During the period 1906–11, Haber's laboratory had the reputation of being the best equipped in the world. Available were an optics room, a high-current laboratory, balance room, library, and several general laboratories besides Haber's private one. The rooms in the one-story structure were sumptuous compared to the dingy cellars used by Sir William Ramsay's students in England.

About forty research workers of about a dozen different nationalities used the facilities. Besides several Germans, there were Norwegians, Poles, Viennese, French, Swiss,

Japanese, Americans, English, Scots, Russians, Australians, and New Zealanders. The Karlsruhe Institute had the usual set of laboratory folk. Among the usual normal workers was the one untidy, unshaved, and frequently dirty. Too, there was the fellow who teased others about their equipment and results, and finally the student who, finding obvious commercial value in his published research, hurried to sell to industry. Haber was displeased about this but never challenged the exit.

Haber preferred to and did speak English or French to students with either native tongue; he knew and sometimes used unprintable idioms in both languages. He spoke slowly and methodically in his capacity as a teacher and adviser. Yet when excited about a topic, he lost sight of his audience. In 1911, he was the annual lecturer of the *Naturforschung* Society in Karlsruhe, speaking about the synthesis of ammonia. The court of the Grand Duchy of Baden had front-row seats; students sat in the rear. Haber started slowly and carefully, but before the end of ten minutes he was immersed in formulas and equations, speaking rapidly. In 1926, he received an English journalist with "courtly manners." He started the conversation in a very quiet and polished style and considerately excused points of view contrary to his own, but after some time, as his enthusiasm heightened, he could not restrain the natural vigor of his expression of opinion. By the end of an hour, he was so "deeply interested in the subject, he had forgotten his theories of style, and was speaking and gesticulating vehemently" in the Haber manner.

At irregularly scheduled weekly meetings students would describe the immediate status of their work, and Haber would suggest and counsel. He walked through the laboratories, saw men in his office, called them together when the interest was for more than one, and used his assistants to carry messages. Once a classroom student accompanying him on a Karlsruhe street asked for an explanation of a physical chemistry problem. Haber drew diagrams on the sidewalk because he had no paper. During the laboratory sessions he had a habit of placing a half-smoked cigar on the laboratory bench; inevitably students followed suit and then carefully watched their butts to prevent an inadvertent exchange.

Haber did not have regular hours for students. Consulting commitments with the *Auergesellschaft*, Koepp and Company, and the Welsbach Company (the *Deutsche Gaslicht Gesellschaft*) frequently took him out of the city. At times his assistants tried to substitute for him. His wife's nephew, Viennese Paul Krassa, was one assistant. When Krassa left, the manner in which Alfred Reis replaced him prompted Haber to remark, "I don't choose my assistants; I confirm them." Gerhard Just, formerly with Max Le Blanc, and Rudolf Leiser had the rank of instructor and directed some research almost alone. American Fred Carter had his final oral examination for his doctor's degree postponed several times because Haber was too busy. Finally, an assistant gave the examination.

Haber's friend Paul Askenasy had charge of about ten of the graduate students. The two had been schoolmates in Breslau. When Askenasy's wife died, he left his industrial post in Vienna and, at Haber's invitation, came to Karlsruhe. Askenasy became editor of the *Zeitschrift für Elektrochemie* after small-in-stature Richard Abegg lost his life in a Gordon Bennett balloon race in 1910.

Haber allowed an Australian to receive a degree, although there was doubt about the man's ability, in the belief that it would be good advertising for Karlsruhe. An American received the doctorate for the same reason. Haber wrote the first United States Nobel prize winner in chemistry, T. W. Richards of Harvard University, for a job for a departing American. He urged a research position, then practically unknown in the United States, for the student. Richards held Haber's opinion in esteem and wanted to create such a staff appointment.

The entire laboratory was welded in devotion to Haber. He was the kind, fatherly friend of all. The intellectual rapport between professor and student gave each man a feeling of security that lasted a lifetime. To a very shy German, Haber said, "I don't know what to make of you because of your bashfulness. But with your character you ought to go places."

The Karlsruhe Chemical Society, virtually dominated by Haber and his co-workers, had several Saturday outings each year. Here Haber's stories were always eagerly awaited. The festivities also included dinner at a neighboring village *Gasthaus*, singing with zest and abandon around a punch bowl in the *Stadtgarten*, some dancing, and the inevitable shop talk. In the winter there was skiing, and during the summer the main activity was walking in the Black Forest. But at all times, the parties were well arranged; a student, Fritz Hiller, often took photographs. At one meeting in the mountains, Haber, after a long climb in hot weather, arrived later than the 10:00 A.M. set by Hiller to take his picture. Haber pointed to a nearby dog and said, "Take ours together; I am as tired as a dog."

Laboratory parties were held at the end of terms. Haber was too busy to take part in all of them. His schedule already necessitated many off-hours visits to the institute. One evening he forgot his keys and entered through a basement window. When he and the student inside left the same way, the watchman mistook them for burglars!

His schedule of work forced abandonment or modification of many of the usual family obligations. Walking with his six-year-old son, he was once heard, in a grave and serious voice, explaining a complex scientific problem. Fortunately, one of young Hermann Haber's greatest delights was watching the institute mechanic at his lathe; this did not tax his father's time. When the King of Saxony visited Karlsruhe, a research student volunteered to take the boy to observe the regal sights; so the child had substitute fatherly attention.

Haber's sister, Helene, had some student companionship while in Karlsruhe. An amiable fellow from Vienna named Gottlieb taught her to ride the bicycle presented by her sister-in-law. She was the only lady allowed to join an occasional forest excursion. Haber took his sister skiing, read Faust to her, and obtained parental permission for her to attend a Karlsruhe school for female artists. He introduced her to a well-known landscape painter, Bisa, often called The Snow Bisa because he did winter scenes. He gave her valuable art lessons. When Helene Haber married a physician and relative of scientist Paul Ehrlich, Haber was a master of fun at the festivities. He spontaneously composed rhymes and told stories. His sister appreciated the poetry, not the tales. He concocted one, for example, wherein Helene, upon becoming engaged, wrote him, "I am to be wed; of course, I am giving up painting."

Haber once acted in a play he wrote to honor the marriage of a colleague, a professor of forestry. He enjoyed the theater, as well as real situations approaching the theatrical. He was amused by the tableau devised by his secretary, *Fraülein* Sachs, a relative of his wife's. The young lady was invited to a masked ball which Dr. August Bernthsen, director of research for the *Badische Anilin und Soda Fabrik*, also attended. She, in mask, drew the scientist into conversation and began to tell him the confidential information discussed by Haber in correspondence with him. Perplexed, Bernthsen immediately left the affair and awaited the first opportunity to talk to Haber. A breach of friendship was prevented when he found there really had been no violation of confidences.

Haber knew the meaning of success several times after 1906. In each instance he experienced a personal broadening and humanizing effect as a result of real achievement. His personality reached a new level of development. For example, he gained self-confidence when he was appointed full professor and director of the Karlsruhe Institute for Physical Chemistry and Electrochemistry. Other organizations also sought him. Fifteen years after being a student at the Federal Polytechnical School in Zurich, Switzerland, he was urged to return as the successor to George Lunge, a flattering offer in itself. The president of the Board of Education of the Zurich canton twice came to Haber in an attempt to persuade him. In July, 1907, the official spoke to the Karlsruhe rector and to Hans Bunte; the result was an increase in salary for Haber.

The ammonia synthesis brought new offers. The *Auergesellschaft* wanted him as director of research. When this did not materialize, the principal owner of the company bestowed an unparalleled honor upon Haber—he gave him his own research institute. Leopold Koppel offered to help build a Kaiser Wilhelm Institute for Physical Chemistry and Electrochemistry on the one condition that Fritz Haber be its head. Haber accepted.

Koppel had founded, early in the twentieth century, the Koppel Foundation "for the purpose of improving the intellectual relations of Germany with other lands." Its first efforts were the maintenance of the German School of Medicine in Shanghai and the American Institute in Berlin.

The foundation was to erect Haber's institute and provide nine thousand dollars a year during the first ten years. The Prussian government donated the property, the starting point in 1913 for a subway to Berlin, and was to give ten thousand dollars a year for the venture. Control was vested in a board consisting of two representatives of the government, two of the Koppel Foundation, and the director Haber. He was to have complete freedom in the choice of research and personnel. The site, Dahlem, had been a large farm belonging to the royal family. At about 1900, it had been subdivided, and lots had been sold for residential purposes. Slowly a suburban community was built.

Haber's new institute was to be part of a great scientific center. The project first received appropriate attention at the centenary celebrations of the University of Berlin in 1910. The idea appealed to Wilhelm II who urged and sponsored the Kaiser Wilhelm Society for the Advancement of Science. Wilhelm II knew the practical value of science. Yet not a single scientist was knighted during his reign. Under Wilhelm I, many, including Hermann Helmholtz and A. W. Hofmann, had been so favored.

The first institute for chemistry was headed by Ernst Beckmann and Richard Willstätter. The second was Haber's. The imperial architect, Ernest von Ihne, was responsible for the design of the first buildings. However, the interiors were mainly the responsibility of the directors. By 1914 seven institutes existed. In 1926 there were thirty, and in the early 1930's, thirty-four. Part of the growth was an expansion of institutes devoted to practical research, i. e., institutes for coal, textiles, and aeronautics.

First president of the Kaiser Wilhelm Society, director of the growing colony at Dahlem, was theologian Adolf von Harnack, author of a *History of Dogma.* A grandson of chemist Justus von Liebig, he was a foremost champion of science. His theory began with the scientist, not the science; he first found a scholar, and then built an institute for him.

Karlsruhe gave Haber a memorable farewell. Early in 1912, a two-day celebration was arranged and conducted by student Fritz Hiller. Seventy-five men, former pupils, some from distant lands, came to a Karlsruhe hotel. At almost every session Haber was in best form with verse and stories. He gave each student a memento of a personally inscribed copper engraving. He had given other farewell gifts previously. Fred Carter, leaving in 1911, received a beautifully bound book containing photographs of all the students. The *Zeitschrift für Elektrochemie,* July, 1911, was dedicated to Haber. The cover appeared to be normal. The inside pages, however, were loaded with jokes, cartoons, verse, and stories commemorating him. Everybody in the institute contributed to the issue. Haber's friend George Bredig, formerly at Heidelberg and then at Zurich in the post Haber had once refused, now succeeded him at Karlsruhe; Askenasy remained at Karlsruhe.

Haber settled in his temporary residence, *Königin Luise Strasse* 14, as a celebrated scientist with students, title, institute, and reputation. The University of Berlin gave him the title of professor. In his new quarters, he continued many of the scientific problems he had started at Karlsruhe. For example, he turned again to gas flames. An assistant at Karlsruhe had resigned in order to devote himself to proving an idea about gas flames that Haber had discounted. After seeing worthwhile results, Haber had been quick to say, "It's a very good thing young people don't listen always to older ones."

One of his first new research projects at Dahlem was undertaken at the request of the Kaiser. He wanted a good indicator for firedamp gas. Germany's huge coal production was always endangered by this menace. A good indicator for poisonous amounts of the gas was necessary.

The miner's safety lamp had its faults. When the proportion of methane, the chief constituent of firedamp gas, exceeded 1 per cent, the flame in the lamp became surrounded by a cap which could be detected only by experienced men. As the amount of gas increased, the cap correspondingly grew in size and visibility. The flame at that point could be dangerous; in fact, more than one-half of the mine explosions were caused by ignition of firedamp.

A new indicator could not very well exploit the chemical properties of methane, since it is inert. And high temperatures are not desirable in a mine because they excite the gas. Therefore, Haber had the difficult problem of finding a reactant which would function only when 1 to 10 per cent of methane was present, one which would be effective at mine temperatures, which would give a clear-cut index, and which would not introduce other dangers. He chose to "appeal not to the eye but the ear, trained to sensitiveness by the silence of the mine."

He and an associate devised a whistle which produced distinctive beats when blown with air containing up to 5 per cent firedamp. Before being used, one side of the whistle was filled with ordinary air; mine air filled the other side. If methane were present, beats would be heard when the whistle was blown. These increased in rapidity with larger amounts of firedamp gas; at the explosive limit there was a characteristic trill.

Haber compared the whistle to the safety lamp: "The lamp has one advantage in that the occurrence of large volumes of irrespirable gas in the air will extinquish the flame, and thus give an automatic danger signal before the risk of asphyxiation actually occurs. In favor of the whistle are its unconditional safety in fire-damp and in the insistent character of its signals, even through considerable distances."

The whistle was hailed as a distinctive advance in major coal mining countries. But widespread use did not follow its introduction and acclaim. Perhaps miners were too accustomed to the safety lamp for the adoption of a new device. But with the whistle Haber joined the ranks of the great scientists in at least one aspect. Just about every great name in physics has published some contribution in acoustic science.

Much of Haber's time was spent in planning the construction of his institute. Accompanied by Gerhard Just, he visited the newly built Muspratt laboratory of physical chemistry in Liverpool, England. He incorporated some features of that institution in his own building.

He gave the Hurter Memorial Lecture before the Liverpool section of the Society of Chemical Industry, November, 1913. His topic was "Modern Chemical Industry." He began his speech before citizens of Germany's commercial rival: "It is impossible to admire too much the richness of inventive genius and the clearness of judgment which the technical chemists . . . developed in your country." When describing the ammonia synthesis he continued with more truth and diplomacy, "I cannot emphasize enough the valuable aid of your countryman, Robert Le Rossignol." At the conclusion of his lecture, he demonstrated the firedamp

whistle and said, "The idea of employing an acoustic apparatus for this purpose was first broached by your fellow
countryman, Professor Forbes in 1880."

Haber knew the immense contributions of English scientists. He realized, too, the gradual failure of British industry
to come close to science. In later years he correctly analyzed
one important factor which gave Germany industrial might.
British industrialists were aloof to their enterprises, save the
money-making aspect. They were not interested in technical
advance, production problems, or theory. The owners seldom heeded the engineer when they employed one; the
latter was considered in a lower class. The English gentle-
man entrepreneur avoided the technician; whereas, the
German industrial system was built, supervised, and maintained by engineers and technicians anxious to have better
processes, cheaper products, and efficiency in every detail. A
close and growing relationship existed between German industry and science; German businessmen and scientists
respected each other for their specialties, and each mutually
profited.

❊

6. The Horrors of Chemical Warfare

❊

WORK AT THE KAISER WILHELM INSTITUTE for Physical Chemistry and Electrochemistry was greatly disorganized during the first few weeks of World War I. Many of the employees were called to service immediately, being members of the reserve corps. Haber volunteered for service and was refused. His resulting depression disappeared when he received a problem from the Ordnance Department. Request was made for gasoline with a low freezing point, since the army expected to fight through a Russian winter. Walther Nernst was also a War Ministry consultant. He was asked to suggest chemical agents which could be included in shrapnel and shell. The material proposed by him, dianisidine chlorosulphonate, an irritant powder, and xylyl bromide, a tear producer, proved ineffective. Haber solved his problem to the satisfaction of the military: Xylene and solvent naptha were efficient anti-freeze substitutes for toluene.

He was next given Nernst's assignment. The job was to find means of scattering chemical agents more effectively. The enemy was to be overcome by them, but advancing troops were not to be hindered. All ten men in the institute worked under Haber's direction on this difficult problem, but many weeks of overtime searching brought no positive result. A disastrous explosion in December, 1914, put an end

66

to the quest. Thermodynamics expert Otto Sackur, co-author with Richard Abegg of a textbook in chemistry, lost his life; Gerhard Just lost an arm.

The idea of a mass discharge of irritant gas from cylinders then gained favor. Since October, the *Auergesellschaft* had been conducting experiments with chlorine in a specially constructed small building. Haber continued and extended these investigations. By the end of January, 1915, the preliminary laboratory research was completed.

The use of poison gas in warfare is known to have occurred during the wars between the Athenians and Spartans in the fifth century B.C., when sulphur fumes were employed against strongly fortified cities. The famous Greek fire, reputedly invented during the late seventh century, was used against the Crusaders by the Saracens. In 1762, bombs emitting asphyxiating fumes were used in the seige of Schweidnitz, a Silesian fortress defended by the Austrians against the Prussians. During the American Civil War, shells filled with phosphorus and sulphur, as well as iron balls heated to red heat, were employed. After the industrial revolution, tear gas saw service in strikes; later the French police used it against the Apaches. By the 1899 Hague Conference, twenty-four nations, including Germany, had agreed not to use asphyxiating gases in warfare. At the 1907 Hague Conference, Great Britain's representative signed the document but Captain Alfred Thayer Mahan of the United States refused. He said it was foolish to prohibit poison gas when big guns and other weapons were indirectly certified for use. During the early months of World War I Russia tried to use chlorine, but in the cold winter the gas formed a less volatile hydrate which sank into the snow. When spring came, the gas reformed and was emitted, but by then the opposing armies were miles away.

Haber realized the value of chlorine. The gas could be a means of driving the Allies out of their trenches and forcing the resumption of open warfare. But he had to convince others before a trial of the weapon could be arranged. He finally found a combat officer who was sympathetic. Captain Peterson allowed one company of his engineer regiment to participate in the test.

Within two months field experiments had been performed to determine the proper humidity and wind conditions; weather of the wrong kind was found capable of making poison gas useless. As Haber said, "When reed grass is merely moved by breezes, one can pack up one's gas equipment and go home."

On April 11, 1915, more than five thousand cylinders of gas were distributed on a three and one-half mile front. Three times inclement weather caused postponement of the attacks. But on April 22, at 4:00 A.M. the holocaust was released. Again at 6:00 A.M., 10:00 A.M., and finally at 5:00 P.M. the deadly stuff was emitted about the sector near Ypres. The greenish-yellow cloud first struck French Algerian troops, who retreated. Some foolhardy French territorial forces and Canadians ran forward against the gas. Most men were horror stricken. They gasped, held their throats, stuffed shawls into their mouths, buried their faces in their shirttails, or burrowed into the ground. Nearly an entire division suffocated in agony. Fifteen thousand casualties were counted; one-third were fatal.

The German victory appeared to be complete. Yet it was not. As Haber explained, "Early in 1915, gas was employed by the German and French sides in small quantities with no results. Then, while we were experimenting with a liquid commonly called a gas because it became effective when it vaporized, I advocated massed gas attacks to break the war's stalemate. But I was a college professor, and therefore not to be heeded by the leaders. They admitted afterward that if they had followed my advice and made a large-scale attack instead of the experiment at Ypres, the Germans would have won."

The military did not know the tactical value of gas; Haber did. He said, "Every new weapon is capable of winning a war. Every war is a war against the soul of the soldier, not the body. New weapons break his morale because they are something new, something he has not experienced, and therefore, something that he fears. We were used to shell fire. The artillery did not do much harm to morale, but the smell of gas upset everybody."

The experimentation continued at Poel and Capelle, a few days after the introduction at Ypres; throughout 1915, chlorine was tested. Several weeks after April 22, prisoners held by the French gave them details of an impending gas offensive. The story evidently circulated for it appeared in the March 30 issue of the *Bulletin of the French Tenth Army* distributed in Picardy. On April 13, a German deserter surrendered to the French near the Ypres sector and told that a gas attack was being planned. A French divisional commander, General Ferry, was impressed by the story and the primitive gas mask shown in its support, but the General's superiors were disbelievers.

At Verdun, in 1916, the German Army attempted a breakthrough by means of gas shelling. When Fritz Haber, supervising the gas detail, delayed because of weather conditions, the officer in charge became impatient. In exasperation, he warned Haber that should the cylinders not be used the next day, favorable or unfavorable wind, they would be sent to the rear; the Allies would not be given more time to learn the troop concentrations. The gas was used.

Almost the same pattern followed the introduction of mustard gas. Haber advised its use only if Germany could win within a year. After that time, he said, the Allies would be able to retaliate. Germany could quickly convert materials used in dyestuffs into mustard gas. Because the Allies did not have a developed organic chemical industry, they would have to invent a new method for making the poison gas. As Haber predicted, twelve months after Germany's first use of the weapon, England and France were employing it with even greater effectiveness. Allied mustard gas was developed by William J. Pope, an English chemist, and the Usine du Rhone dye plant in France; it was perfected by the Levenstein dye works in England.

At first German troops had an improvised gas mask of wadding soaked with alkali. Haber prodded his laboratory workers. "Gentlemen, we must make masks," he told them repeatedly. Germany had no open supply line to sources of natural rubber, and synthetic material had to be used for the masks. Within six months after beginning the drive for a mask, a suitable respirator was manufactured.

Haber also directed research seeking to learn the toxic effects of poison gas. Laboratory animals succumbed first to phosgene. Lewisite and mustard gas were equally toxic, while chlorine was by far the weakest poison. As expected, a large increase in concentration was required for death when the time of exposure was reduced below ten minutes.

Gas actually proved to be a weak weapon. The 125,000 tons of gas used by both sides during the war caused less than 5 per cent of the total casualties of 21,250,000. Two and one-half per cent of those affected by gas died; on the other hand, 25 per cent of the casualties from bullets and high explosives were fatal. Yet the odium attached to poison gas persists; to this day, it is believed a ghastly weapon.

Mrs. Clara Haber was vitally affected by her husband's role in gas warfare. She knew what chemical fumes were; she knew their suffocating nature. Poison gas used on a mass scale was revolting to her; chemical warfare was an avenue or excuse for the morbid worry she seemed to favor. It was conducive to the extension of anxiety and melancholy.

Her husband's easygoing attitude toward money was another cause of anxiety. Despite her warnings that he might come to bodily harm, he would come home with bulging pockets of currency—paid for consulting services. She felt strongly, too, about his spending more than his income. He was optimistic, expecting the nitrogen-fixation process to earn large amounts of money—which it did, and which he spent and gave freely.

Since the early days at Karlsruhe even ordinary things depressed her. She reflected and meditated on subjects which others would have given little further thought. Laden with preoccupation, her appearance and mannerisms better fitted a much older woman.

She began to regard poison gas not only as a perversion of science but also as a sign of barbarism. It brought back the tortures men said they had forgotten long ago. It degraded and corrupted the discipline which had opened new vistas of life. Clara Haber pleaded with her husband to forsake poison gas. She presented facts. She asked in the name of human sympathy and kindliness. She brought forth all the sentiments and feelings with which women stir men. Finally, she quit protesting and demanded that Fritz Haber have no part in the nefarious business.

He was adamant to all his wife's pleas, although he, too, hated the idea of its use. After the first gas attack he had suffered a trauma. But in German hands, he said, the weapon could bring quick victory. He told his wife that a scientist

71

belongs to the world during times of peace but to his country during times of war. He could not effectively, he said, be a world citizen during periods of stress; and not to help his country with all his power was tantamount to self-destruction. He fought for a triumphant Germany, one whose might would enforce justice and order, preserve culture, and cultivate science.

Stubbornly, Haber overruled his wife's every suggestion. The argument was serious and no gentle reconciliation followed. Both stalked away convinced of their positions. Had Clara reflected and reasoned, she might have decided on separation or divorce. She might have striven to attain recognition once more as Dr. Clara Immerwahr, scientist and welfare worker for the world. As such she could probably have overcome any taint which the name of Haber and its attendant suggestion of poison gas had inflicted upon her. But she was not thinking logically, and she acted in the heat of argument following a period of emotional involvement.

Fritz Haber went to the eastern front to supervise the installation of gas cylinders. That evening Clara Haber committed suicide.

In 1916, Haber became chief of the newly formed Chemical Warfare Service, a department of the War Ministry. Every detail of chemical offense and defense, supply, and research came under his supervision. When a new poison gas was introduced, he arranged conferences so that manufacturing plants could be used to their best advantage; mustard gas, for example, was first processed at Ludwigshafen and brought to Leverkusen for final perfection. He directed work on coal production refinements, pressure syntheses of organic materials, and metal improvements. When the Allied blockade made the acquisition of raw ma-

terials difficult, when deadly gases made defense more perplexing, when the situation demanded speed and executive
talent, he was outstanding.

No one in Germany had properly estimated the condition
which would occur by a complete blockade of the country.
Also, military calculations had been based upon the experiences of the last war, with France in 1870. These were soon
shown to be in error; the quantities of materials needed were
a tremendous multiple of what had been expected. Some of
the acquisition of materials was Haber's job.

He had unexpected aid in supplying nitrogen compounds.
Fifty thousand tons of Chilean nitrate were left intact in
Antwerp by retreating Belgians. They could have dumped
it into the Schelde River along with other valuables; either
oversight or ignorance gave Germany the stockpile. Allied
and Central Power generals who did not know the importance of nitrogen fertilizers should have known it after the
naval battle, in the fourth month of the war, off the Falkland
Islands, near the coast of Chile.

Mass production of fertilizers through his nitrogen-fixation process was largely the work of others. His English
collaborator, Le Rossignol, married to a Karlsruhe young
lady, lived in Berlin; he was released from internment at
Haber's request. Neither he nor Haber had a major part in
the commercial application of the discovery.

The *Badische* Company had a great deal of confidence in
the ammonia synthesis—they sold their arc process interests
in Norway soon after obtaining the Haber patents. In 1910,
they had constructed a pilot plant, a test unit, at Ludwigshafen, the industrial city across the Rhine River from the
community of Mannheim, not far from Karlsruhe. Here they
solved three major difficulties: One was the building of
apparatus strong enough to withstand high pressures and

temperatures not far from red heat; second was overcoming the danger of serious explosions; third was the problem finding satisfactory catalysts. Mittasch and his helpers had investigated more than ten thousand different substances as speed-up agents. He and Haber became enthusiastic about the role of such promoters, and they hoped to issue a handbook about catalytic reactions.

Purification of the reacting gases proved to be a major portion of the cost. At first, about 75 per cent of the total production expense went into the preparation of mixtures of hydrogen and nitrogen. The problems involving high pressure, possible explosions, and catalysts were perplexing but not costly.

In 1911, the *Badische* Company built an ammonia synthesis factory at Oppau in the same Rhineland section. In September, 1913, production started with an initial output of about seven thousand tons of nitrogen a year. During the war the Oppau plant had a yearly capacity of about sixty thousand tons of fixed nitrogen. The research laboratory, five stories high, was the largest and best equipped industrial one in Germany with a staff of 250 chemists. In May, 1916, the *Badische* Company began to build their famous Leunawerk, near Merseburg in the lignite region. An Allied observer who inspected the completed factory confessed the sight made him feel proud of the human race, despite its being an enemy's accomplishment. In 1918, the Haber process provided Germany with more than two hundred thousand tons of nitrogen compounds. It was the factor which more than any other gave the Kaiser staying power after America's entry into the war. It showed more than any other one thing that modern war is largely an affair of industrial production.

Haber received decorations and honors for his work. He

became a Knight of both classes of the Iron Cross as well as a Knight of the Kaiser House Order of Hohenzollern Swords. He was given the Order of the Crown Third Class and an autographed portrait of Wilhelm II. The Grand Duke of Baden presented him with a First Class Red Cross as well as knighthood in a regal order. He was made an honorary fellow of the Bayer Academy of Science in Munich and also of the Prussian and Göttingen Academies. Honorary doctor's degrees were conferred upon him by Göttingen University, the University of Wittenberg, later absorbed by the University of Halle, and the Karlsruhe Engineering College. He started the Haber foundation for the cultivation of physical chemistry, with a donation of $12,000, at his former place of employment.

One of Haber's great disappointments was lack of a higher military title. As a full professor at a university, he had the feeling he was equivalent to a general; academy members had a comparable uniform for court occasions. Thus as a sergeant wearing a special uniform, he was ill at ease. To his guide in Belgium he said, "Look at me in this disguise and don't laugh too much."

Haber was ambitious for the Legion of Merit award. He was on the list of prospective recipients when the armistice came. Too, he hoped to become a member of the General Staff. Early in 1915, he was made a captain. Promotion from a reserve sergeant major of cavalry and artillery directly to captain had never before been accomplished within the German Army. But his English, French, and American equivalents in chemical warfare were generals. Even as a captain, he was uncertain in his relations to the higher ranks of the military. He asked about the salute and how to behave upon presentation to such officers. He knew one value of his rank, and even as a sergeant he chose to use rank. When his friend Richard Willstätter hesitated to join in gas mask research, Haber said, "I am a sergeant. I command you to the task."

The title of captain placed him in an unfavorable position. He could never speak openly to a senior officer who was unreasonable. In dealing by letter, the title of captain did not have much weight. Some commanders would detail underlings to negotiate with him. The delay of transactions via messengers irritated and disgusted him. Often he would proceed to the War Ministry and try to give orders as he wanted them.

Once Captain Haber played General Haber and accomplished his end immediately. He asked the president of the National Health Institute for laboratory space. One man at the conference said, "It may be that the government may ask us to do research and we would need the laboratory." Haber replied, "I am the War Ministry. If I say we need this for gas research, then the War Ministry will not say tomorrow that we need this for something else." He made other self-appointments. Early in August, 1914, he and two assistants entered a neighboring Dahlem institute and asked the director what he could do for the war. Haber was without authority.

He wanted a higher rank to be a more efficient public servant, not for any military inclinations. He joked about uniforms and decorations; he disliked war. Peace, he said, would be when one could sleep in a bed and not be afraid of soldier-loving rats and lice. In jest, he produced a delousing certificate upon returning from the eastern front; friends were thus assured they would be safe when dining with him. He had no high regard for the military. "The intellect of the army man," he later evaluated, "trained in the command of troops, lacked the technical imagination to appreciate the changing conduct of war with its technical developments. Without this imagination, preparation followed historic lines. The measure of the needs, and the methods of fulfilling them, were taken from the experience of the past, in which the technical requirements were different."

He was precise in excoriating the pretensions and blunders of the military mind. His war stories almost always pointed to this moral. His account, for example, of how he lived to become a hero was a subtle criticism: He and several officers were walking across a battlefield. Suddenly, they found themselves in the line of fire. The men, except Haber, fell to the ground. He, wearing three overcoats to keep warm, continued. He knew that with the weight of the coats he would not be able to raise himself from the horizontal position. Rather than lie down and possibly freeze to death, he preferred to go forward. Generals, too, had his condemnation. One of his favorite tales concerned the high officer he met in a roadway. Asked how the war was going, the general did not know. He did not know what to do or what was going on; he was a most helpless man. Haber's stories had elements of truth; for instance, there was a captain attached to his staff who had the habit of wearing spurs although he had a desk assignment. The officer invariably appeared in the riding accessory. At a meeting one day, Haber addressed the man, "Captain, jump on your horse and ride into the next room for the documents."

Haber respected very few military traits. One he did admire was the ability of soldiers to fall asleep for a few minutes at any time of day or night. About the only army man with whom he was friends was Colonel Max Bauer, a technician with Ludendorff. But Haber had little time for building new friendships. He even used the twenty-minute drive from Dahlem to the War Ministry for business purposes. He also maintained a suite at the Adlon Hotel when obligations kept him in the city.

The *Deutsche Klub* of 1914 was close to the Adlon Hotel. One of its special features was a magnificent library. Miss Charlotta Nathan was the general secretary; she was the only lady admitted among the male members. Miss Nathan had many social accomplishments without the benefit of a university education. She was a woman of presence, who knew how to meet people. She was alert and witty, brilliant, and quick in repartee.

Fritz Haber met short, blonde Charlotta Nathan through the courtesy of a rainstorm. She loaned him an umbrella. When returning it, he said, "I lay the umbrella into your arms and myself and my thanks at your feet." She answered, "I'd rather like the contrary." During the spring of 1917, he began seeing her outside the club. He became passionately fond of her, experiencing again the joy and exhilaration of love. At forty-nine he found himself enamored of a woman slightly more than half his age.

Fritz Haber proposed marriage. Surprised, Miss Nathan suggested such a solution would not be feasible. With the difference in years, she protested that it was a risky undertaking, regardless of the overpowering attraction. Gallantly, he contradicted her and won her to his point of view. He prepared to fight in the event his friends did not completely accept her.

When his son Hermann had a one-day leave from his duties as an emergency farmer, Haber indicated the new arrangements to him. He took the fifteen-year-old boy and Miss Nathan to the club for dinner and to a moving picture theater afterward. He prepared to follow in the footsteps of his father, who as a widower with a young son married a nineteen-year-old woman.

78

Fritz Haber married Charlotta Nathan in the fall of 1917, two and one-half years after the death of his first wife. Happiness seemed to be his once more. His wife was enthusiastic in sharing his views and interests. She rose to the occasion of her position by responding over the telephone as Frau *Geheimrat* Haber. (His first wife had answered Frau Haber or Frau Professor Haber.) Haber was now content and satisfied; the new Mrs. Haber helped give him one of the most joyful periods of his life.

✠

7. Postwar Adjustment

✠

IN THE SUMMER OF 1918, Haber and many other Germans knew that the war was lost. The Allied use of tanks and the entry of the United States proved to be decisive factors. A defeated Germany meant a defeated Haber. Many friends believed him "75 per cent dead." He had put all his hopes and energies into the struggle; he had associated himself completely and wholeheartedly with his country. Victory would have given him an extraordinary world position. Defeat gave him total pain.

As the armistice was being signed at Compiègne, France, he, completely depressed, asked a friend and his wife to spend an evening with him. He was beaten in spirit; he was bewildered. Germany had won most of the battles during the four-year war. In the last offensive, lasting until May, the Marne River had been reached and the channel ports had been very close. Haber was given one solace: Many returning soldiers claimed that lack of materiel alone lost the war. They said Germany would rise again. He listened sympathetically to the prediction of another war in twenty years.

During the war, Haber had begun to suffer from a ductless gland disturbance. His pituitary gland—the pituiary is also known as the hypophysis, from the Geek term for "lying under," describing the gland's position under the brain—was not functioning properly. Lack of one of the many hormones produced by the gland gave Haber the symptoms of *diabetes insipidus*. The rare disease necessitated his drinking enormous amounts of water; companions wondered and sometimes inquired why he drank eight to ten glasses of water at a time. His friend August von Wasserman, after whom the test for syphilis is named, made the prognosis that Haber was a lost man; his life would be limited and sickly. In his youth, Haber told his wife, he had suffered fainting spells and headaches after falling into a deep hole while balancing on a log; he had spent some time in a rest home trying to get relief. He now frequently was his own physician, experimenting with remedies and becoming acquainted with many medical problems. One doctor credited him with restating a difficulty more clearly than ever had been done before.

Bitter Allied criticism of his war work added to his discomfort and unhappiness. During 1914–18, enemy censure was to be expected. When he and Karl Bosch had received the Bunsen Society gold medal (then made of iron), the editors of the *Journal of Industrial and Engineering Chemistry* made pointed comments. They called for careful consideration of admittance into the good fellowship of science all the evil scientists of Germany, especially those responsible for poison gas. Shortly after the United States had entered the war, Wilhelm Ostwald's and Emil Fischer's honorary memberships in the American Chemical Society had been revoked; only two members of the board of directors had opposed their expulsion.

The armistice stopped physical warfare; vituperation continued. Many German leaders were indicted but never tried. The only men brought to trial at Leipzig held relatively

81

obscure positions in the Kaiser's government. Six were convicted, receiving short terms, and most "escaped" shortly after imprisonment. Believing himself a potential war criminal, Haber grew a beard as a disguise and went to Switzerland for several weeks; he was afraid of being delivered to the Allies. His name was on the list of 895 names presented by the Entente on February 7, 1920.

Soon after the war, Major Victor Lefebre published a book, *The Riddle of the Rhine,* in which he charged Haber with war preparations and a search for poison gas in late 1914; for substantiation, he quoted a worker at Haber's institute. British chemist Sir Edward Thorpe, reviewing the volume for *Nature,* underscored these charges despite the report of a British mission visiting Germany that it found that "no arrangements appear to have been made prior to the outbreak of the war to utilize the resources of any of the dye factories."

Haber replied to these claims: "Perhaps there might have been some grounds for suspicion if Germany could have foreseen the trench warfare and if we could have imagined the German troops could be held up for weeks and months before the enemy's wire entanglements. But previous to the war, and up to the Battle of the Marne, everyone in Germany imagined that the course of the war would be a succession of rapid marches and great pitched battles, and what use would gas have been to a field army in such a war of movements? . . . We had actually first to read in the French, Italian, and English press . . . of the terrible things that were in preparation for us before we began to make similar preparations in view of the commencement of the war of position.

"In war men think otherwise than they do in peace and many a German during the stress of war may have adopted the British maxim, 'My country, right or wrong,' but that German science and industry before the war made preparations with deliberate intent for gas warfare against other nations is an assertion that in the interest of the necessary interdependence of the nations in the realms of science and industry, must not be allowed to go uncontradicted in so serious and respected a journal as *Nature*."

On the morning of September 21, 1921, the synthetic ammonia plants of the *Badische* Company at Oppau, employing 5,200 persons, were blown up by an explosion that completely wrecked the town of Oppau and a neighboring village. Casualties were high. Many foreign newspapers took the catastrophe as a sign of Germany's continuing search for war weapons, and renewed poison gas accusations. *The New York Times* suggested that experimentation of a secret nature had been going on at the Oppau factory, which, they recalled, "manufactured most of the chlorine and phosgene used by the Germans in their gas attacks during the war." An American reporter interviewed Haber and brought away his reminiscences of the war.

Upon the tenth anniversary of the Kaiser Wilhelm Society in 1922, *Nature,* surveying the record of a decade's work, charged, "It will not be forgotten that it was at the Kaiser Wilhelm Institute for the Promotion of Science that *Geheimrat* Haber made his experiments on poison gas, prior to the Battle of Ypres, which initiated a mode of warfare which is to the everlasting discredit of the German."

Others remembered that in Karlsruhe Haber had been depicted as Hamlet in a graveyard, leaning on a gas cylinder and holding a skull. The caricature, drawn in 1904 at a Christmas party, was intended to show his interest in gas chemistry and his diversion to dramatics. Soon after the war it was subject to different interpretation. Even many years later, an Allied scientist chose to point out Haber in a photograph by drawing a gas mask over his face.

Haber and a colleague, as representatives of the German Chemical Society, went to France for a science conference. His companion was welcomed, but Haber was coldly received, many Frenchmen refusing to shake his hand.

Haber's reaction to the poison gas charges was at first little more than his letter to *Nature* and a restatement of counter claims; i.e., the French were the first users; the Allies had not made a diplomatic protest; every new weapon is scored as barbaric. German apologists could cite more facts: The Allies should have been aware of the possibilities. In 1913, Germany had fifteen thousand chemical factories; the country produced 75 per cent of the world's dyes. It had the industrial potential for chemical warfare.

As Haber visited foreign countries and spoke to Allied subjects, he became more sensitive to the accusations. He no longer gave dispassionate facts about a force emotionally affecting most people. He cited the power of other weapons. Airplanes carrying high explosives, he predicted, would kill great numbers of people and do much havoc. Civilian populations would be exposed to the dangers of war. Yet the airplane would be glorified, rather than condemned, because it was a return to individual combat, less distasteful to the people. The submarine, he said, had been less censured because it operated out of sight.

He knew that he and other German leaders were subject to being accused as war criminals, but he could not visualize himself guilty of any atrocity. Indeed, he often wondered how some sordid war tale he heard could be true. He could not understand, for example, that Bavarians bringing up French prisoners could "dispose" of them. The story went

A Schlenk Photograph of Fritz Haber at Dahlem

COURTESY MRS. MARGARET W. BRUCH

Fritz Haber's Mother, Paula Haber

COURTESY MRS. EVA ROST

that the prisoner line was shortened because routing and feeding of prisoners proved to be too difficult.

Haber came to dislike all discussion of poison gas. When the subject was mentioned, some foreigners received the impression that he tried to explain away any guilt and to make clear that all had been a grievous error. In Osaka, Japan, he later said, "All the English papers in Japan seem to be misunderstanding the question of poison gas."

Most scientists before and after Haber have worked diligently on war weapons. Leonardo da Vinci was paid for knowing about the art of fortification. Galileo calculated projectile paths and tried to sell the telescope as a useful device for the military. Very few scientists refused to work on the development of the atomic bomb, although some did petition President Truman not to drop it on inhabited areas. During the Crimean War, the British government had asked Michael Faraday about the feasibility of using poison gas. Faraday had said that it was entirely feasible but that it was inhuman, and he would have nothing to do with it. Only recently has Faraday's position been echoed by additional scientists aware of a social responsibility to mankind.

Because of his work with poison gas, Haber's is the only Nobel prize in science that has ever been contested. In November, 1919, he was awarded the 1918 chemistry prize. Frenchmen offered awards declined the honor rather than be in the same company with their former enemy. One French scholar accused the Swedes—the Swedish Academy, of course, selects Nobel prize winners—of manufacturing gas masks for the German army. Another called Haber "morally unfit for the honor and material benefits of a Nobel prize." Protests were equally articulate in the United States and in England. Haber, user of poison gas, was not entitled to a reward established by Nobel, inventor of dynamite.

He and four other German Nobel prize winners—Max von Laue, Max Planck, Johannes Stark, and Richard Willstätter—went to Stockholm for the ceremonies. The group was greeted by five journalists, one for each man. The scientists were not prepared to answer the questions they were asked; politics and international relations were far from their specialties. The journalists became noticeably disturbed and dissatisfied. Haber, with a dramatic gesture, took what seemed to be a manuscript from his coat pocket and read it in a sonorous voice. His statement was very long and the newspaperwoman assigned to him became weary in her notetaking. The next day the interviews were published, and Haber's lengthy speech was divided into five parts; each scientist had been credited with a portion. None of them could read Swedish and they never found out which of Haber's opinions they had been given. Perhaps in return for his co-operation and unintended generosity towards his colleagues he was pictured as having a magnificent and full head of hair. He was then as bald as a billiard ball.

Haber continued to devote his energies to Germany during the early postwar period. He suggested acetylene as a substitute for gasoline to aid Germany's petroleum shortage. Simple operations with coal, abundant in Germany, yielded the gas. In 1919 he helped organize technicians and engineers for public service. The men were trained to operate utilities in the event of a strike; the precaution was necessary in those dire days.

A more notable achievement was his work with the *Notgemeinschaft der Deutschen Wissenschaft,* the Emergency Society for German Science. He made eloquent appeals for its founding and successful operation. "Above everything, save Germany's scientific institutions," he said. "We shall need them now more than ever." Committees in twenty-one divisions of natural science, under the effective leadership of Haber and others, formed the simple administration for the relief agency. Applications for aid were to be reviewed at monthly meetings. Grants for research were to be given, fellowships established, apparatus bought, exchanged, and distributed, scientific literature obtained from other countries, and worthy noncommercial manuscripts published. Funds were raised in Germany and abroad. Allied governments and business corporations made donations. Japan gave one million yen. The General Electric Company of the United States was a contributor. When not enough money was available for a project, Haber had other suggestions. He said, "The best, the most beautiful, and the most expensive apparatus is just good enough for a scientific investigator. But when it cannot be procured at all by any and all means, then indeed reason and intuition have to replace the technology that is absent." He was, to be sure, a rationalist as well as an experimentalist.

He had his own financial problems coincident with securing support for German science. The crippling inflation that followed the war destroyed the worth of his unusual patent royalty arrangement. The amount he received for every kilogram of product sold became very small in real value. If he had had the customary percentage contract, the crisis would not have seriously affected his income. Fortunately, the *Badische* Company agreed to replace the arrangement with a more equitable one.

The Margulies Company of Vienna sued for a share of his royalties, claiming that it had not instructed him to stop research on the ammonia synthesis. Haber's attorneys demonstrated that the company's refusal to co-operate with monetary support was tantamount to a cease order.

87

Haber took up another monetary burden at a time when it appeared not too foolish. Speculation with securities seemed one way to avoid the insecurity of a fluctuating currency. He thought he would have advance financial information because he was well acquainted in governmental and industrial circles. Yet the venture was a failure; it became a loss of time and money. His wife learned to be a patient examiner of newspaper market quotations each morning. He became a wiser amateur economist. At one time he purchased three thousand shares of an Argentine security at $1,200 a share. When the price fell to $1,000, a banker friend, O. Schweitzer, advised him to sell. Haber still had possession of the stock when the market value dropped to $208 a share.

Inheritances balanced some losses. His father's brother, Edward, cremated in Bremen, left his American-won fortune and materials. Fritz Haber's portion of the estate was small. Some of the nephews and grand-nephews received such items as trousers reputedly strong enough to walk by themselves. However, in 1920, Haber received a share of his father's estate. His fortune was sizable and included property in Breslau. Siegfried Haber had sold his business and lived on the interest from investments until after the age of eighty. At seventy-seven he had been active enough to direct the wartime distribution of potatoes in Silesia.

Haber brought a friend, Friedrich Epstein, to Siegfried Haber's funeral. He introduced this scientist as an undertaker to several Breslau residents. One of the women was sensitive and taken aback at the extended remarks about death and cremation. The nonchalant conversation about stuffing, painting, draining blood, and dipping in formaldehyde was repugnant to her. But the hoax was maintained.

Haber and Epstein enjoyed the practical joke; others had to inform the victim later how she had been duped.

Haber endured no real financial insecurity, however. His income was large; besides royalties and inheritances, he received consultant's fees and a salary. His residence, *Faradayweg* 8, near the subway station, *Thielplatz*, Dahlem, was rent free.

Unsettled conditions prompted him and his neighbors to form an auxiliary volunteer police force. He had a safe for valuables in his bedroom as well as the firearms which almost every family purchased, for a mere trifle, from returned soldiers. Despite these precautions, the front door of his twelve-room house was pried open one night, and two Oriental rugs and a carpet were stolen. Fortunately they were insured, but the crime was never solved.

To protect against another robbery before the lock could be repaired, he and his son Hermann took turns guarding the door each night from 10:00 P.M. until 2:00 A.M. and from 2:00 A.M. until 6:00 A.M. Later Haber installed a burglar-alarm system and purchased a watchdog. The animal was unfriendly to anyone not a regular member of the household.

During the prewar years at Dahlem he had enjoyed two dogs, a shepherd and a Saint Bernard. The former fought with the shepherd of his neighbor and friend at *Faradayweg* 10, Richard Willstätter. Haber, in jest, accused the other shepherd of insulting remarks and provoking argument. But he disposed of this dog. The Saint Bernard remained until the war.

Haber did not really need a watchdog. He himself made a good watchdog, as had earlier been proved. His son came home at a late hour one night to find his father on the staircase with a rifle, commanding: "Come with your hands up or I'll shoot." Later in the year, Hermann Haber chose to enter at a similar hour through a second-floor window. He had the help of the gardener's ladder. Perhaps not wanting it to be used again for a like purpose, he placed it in his father's study. Early in the morning, Haber was pounding on his son's bedroom door demanding to know what the gardener's ladder was doing in his library.

8. Search for Gold

✠

THE ALLIES demanded reparations from Germany—thirty-three billion dollars. One-quarter billion was to be paid in gold immediately or with notes maturing in three months. One favored solution within Germany for gathering this enormous sum was to start a new industry. The exploitation of the synthetic ammonia process was another suggestion. But the possibility of large royalties was gone. Allied industrial nations had already purchased the patents or had confiscated them as war booty and had established their own similar fixation systems. Likewise the dye industry could not serve as a large revenue collector for the same reason. The German colonies were lost; their service could no longer be considered. Yet Haber believed Germany could make her remaining part of the African Sudan flourish by the use of artificial fertilizers.

He often expressed the sum specified by the victors as fifty thousand tons of gold. He had in mind, too, an estimate of the total gold content of the oceans—eight billion tons. When he had been in Stockholm to receive the Nobel prize, Haber had spoken to scientist Svante Arrhenius about the gold in sea water. The idea of getting the mineral out of the sea was Arrhenius'.

In 1819, an English physician, Dr. Alexander Marcet, and

in 1865, a Danish chemist, Professor Johann Georg Forchhammer, obtained almost identical results in analyses of the
constituents of the ocean water. Forchhammer had worked
twenty years to analyze about two hundred samples of
water. From 1872 to 1876, *H.M.S. Challenger* carried scientific personnel on a cruise to study the oceans. On board
was a German-born chemist, Professor William Dittmar,
who analyzed seventy-seven samples over a period of years,
and he, too, came to comparable conclusions. None of the
three investigations was primarily concerned with elements present in minute concentrations—such as gold.

Haber surveyed nine previous investigations of gold in sea
water and found that all had detected approximately the
same quantity of gold in different geographical areas. Determinations made as far apart as the Isle of Man, in 1872,
and the Bay of San Francisco, in 1894, had given the same
general figure—five to ten milligrams of gold per metric ton
of sea water. Some samples contained nearly twice as much
as the lowest-grade land deposit which would be profitable
to operate. Haber accepted the smallest amount reported
as a guide. He did not check the published results.

He became convinced that the wealth in the sea water
could pay the Allies. But he had difficulty instilling a similar
belief in associates and friends. Many argued that the published data was erroneously high; others saw folly in any
attempt to scour the oceans for gold. Their arguments did
not change Haber's mind. Perhaps he was influenced by his
previous conquest of the seemingly impossible. Further,
many achievements of note have been first scorned as impossible or foolish. His nitrogen-fixation process extracted
wealth from the air; maybe a repeat performance would
mean wealth from the sea.

Haber took action. Laboratory work for *Meerforschung,*

sea investigation, was done in a closed section of the institute called Department M. At first, the project was kept secret, primarily to avoid a fall in the price of gold in the event of success—spending a few hundredths of a cent for every ton of water processed.

Extraction schemes were devised without previously ascertaining the exact form in which gold is present in ocean water—actually the element is seldom found uncombined. Synthetic sea water was used in developing methods of gold removal. A special barracks adjacent to the institute was the experimental factory. Metal was avoided in this pilot plant in order to prevent the addition of impurity, however minute; basins, pumps, and tubing were earthenware. The recovery procedure of filtering after bubbling in the gas sulfur dioxide proved inefficient—only 35 per cent of the added gold was recovered. A more successful process involved the addition of lead acetate or mercuric nitrate followed by ammonium sulfide. The gold in sea water, captured as a metallic sulfide, was recovered by differential washing. The vessel was first rinsed by water at a speed which would not disturb; then water from the opposite direction stirred and agitated; finally, relatively little water washed off the precipitate. The separation of silver and platinum from the gold was a minor difficulty. Platinum, present in very minute amounts, was neglected; silver was dissolved by nitric acid and lead acetate.

Haber sought more financial support after this extraction method was perfected. He found friendly financiers in Frankfurt; here the *Gold und Silber Scheide Anstalt,* a refining company, gave aid; even greater support came from the *Metalbank* in the same city. The latter financial institution supplied valuable foreign currency as well as technical help and laboratory facilities through its allied company, the

Metallgesellschaft. The Hamburg-American Line agreed to install an analytical laboratory and extraction plant on one of its ships. A model of the assigned cabin was prepared at Dahlem. The twenty-square-meter replica was used to plan a well-equipped laboratory; electricity, steam, distilled water, and compressed air were installed. Contact with the metal of the ship was avoided; hard rubber tubing brought in the sea water.

In July, 1923, throughout the voyage to New York, none of the *Hansa*'s 932 passengers knew or could guess correctly the activities of the laboratory, on the main deck near the companionway. Three chemists, W. Zisch, F. Matthias, and H. Eisner, were able to maintain operations twenty-four hours a day by working in shifts. They cared for the extraction apparatus and made analyses. It took about an hour to determine the amount of gold in a quart of water.

Haber supervised and occasionally helped with the work. Often he would measure on the ship's bridge the diameter of the small gold-silver balls obtained. The vibrations of the boat and the laboratory's higher temperature made these determinations difficult.

He was met by newspaper reporters in New York harbor. He refused to give any specific information, but said that the tests performed might result in a great discovery. Some students aboard told the newspapermen that the experiments were an attempt to obtain electricity from water; others on board conjectured a corrosion investigation. Fantastic guesses included a study of the forces to halt ships (because the *Hansa* had stopped twice en route) and a search for easy ways to color water. One journalist noted Haber's suit of cheap material. Haber enjoyed this observation and joked about asking for a rectification of the story, for his clothes in those days of inflation in Germany cost several thousand marks. Another newspaperman reported seeing Haber in the food line with dishwashers and other crew members. He and his collaborators were on the ship's articles as assistant pursers at a salary of 100,000 marks a month, or about 8 cents in United States money.

Haber disliked and suffered from the intense heat, so he stayed at the more comfortable Hotel Astor in Times Square while the three chemists lived on the *Hansa*. He visited a former student in Newark, New Jersey, the Rockefeller Institute, and the General Electric Company in Schenectady; he readily told colleagues that he was searching the seas for gold. One day, on leaving his hotel for Washington, D.C., he was surprised not to be detained when he failed to stop to pay his bill. He inquired of the proprietor, a member of an established Frankfurt family, the reason for this apparent laxity. He was told that the number of persons escaping payment of hotel bills proved so small that to trouble ten thousand others walking out with traveling bags would be a loss and perhaps an affront. Fritz Haber was pleased to hear this application of statistics to business.

The *Hansa* made a second trip after the extraction apparatus was fitted with a copper filter made to order in New York City; the first iron filter was worn by sea water. Haber remained in Dahlem and received results via a special code. Believing more gold would be present in warm waters, he arranged a third voyage on the liner *Württemberg*, going from Hamburg to Buenos Aires. This South Atlantic cruise was in part financed by the *Notgemeinschaft* and the Reichsmarine Expedition. Haber found a new friend in the skipper, Captain Frank. He was also initiated into the Order of Neptune when crossing the equator. In the colorful ceremonies, he was dubbed "The Alchemist." His sacrifice, together with a dip into the South Atlantic, was three bottles of wine to

King Neptune. He asked for a return of the empty containers as well as permission to take sea water samples.

Haber was still confident that the extraction process would be successful. In December, 1923, in an address before the German Club of Buenos Aires, he said at the end, "He who loses his hair shall become crowned." But the South Atlantic did not yield the expected amounts of gold.

Haber requested and received sea water samples from all sections of the world. Ten thousand half-gallon bottles were dispatched and returned. German ship captains, foreign fishery bureaus, naturalists, and volunteers aided. With this varied assistance, both mischievous and inadvertent errors occurred. One Dutch prankster mailed a container of copper sulphate solution.

Sample analyses, which should have come first, showed smaller amounts of gold than anticipated. The largest quantity was found off the coast of Spain, near Cabo de Gata: nine milligrams per ton. But the great percentage of other samples yielded tenths of hundredths of this sizable yield.

Haber began to lose hope after the South Atlantic voyage. The quest no longer justified large-scale work. A fourth expedition, to the North Sea, went without him. By 1926, he had lost faith in the idea. In 1927, the project was a dying ember when a chemist at the institute made a fifth voyage; crossing the Atlantic on the *Meteor,* this scientist made a final check of values.

Haber's disappointment was severe. A planned monograph on the topic never reached the writing stage. Only two reports were submitted to scientific journals. In the first, the analytical method was described. The second gave data for a large portion of the work and concluded that gold could not be economically recovered from sea water.

One of his chief aides in the investigation published a

96

more comprehensive report in 1935. He listed gold concentrations in every major body of water. Samples collected off the coast of Newfoundland, where the Labrador current meets the Gulf Stream, had the highest content; those from South Atlantic waters had the lowest. The total amount of ocean gold, even after Haber established the correct concentration at thousandths of milligrams instead of whole milligrams per ton, is very large—about eight micrograms per ton of water. The cost of extraction could be lowered by searching for veritable islands of the metal, because the oceans are not homogeneous in gold content. But rules for finding these concentrated areas are unknown. As Haber said, the search for them would be equivalent to looking for schools of herring; furthermore, the islands of gold could disappear during an analysis.

Haber thought the investigation would have value in oceanography. Today this is a fact; then it was a rationalization. The work contributed to oceanography through the science of analysis. A hitherto unsurpassed technique for gold assay was devised. One one-hundred-millionth of a gram of gold in a quart of water could be detected with a possible error of 3 per cent. This remarkable analytical acuity had its first application in 1925. A German scientist studying mercury quartz lamps announced the conversion of mercury into gold; he had achieved one of the dreams of the alchemists. He was invited to speak at Dahlem, where he demonstrated and described the process. Haber was deeply impressed, along with a number of others present. With gravity and emphasis, Haber quoted Goethe, *"Mein Herren, wir sind dabeit gewesen."* (Gentlemen, we were present.) He expected it to be a revolutionary discovery; the assembled scientists were to feel honored to be witnesses. But results from sea prospecting disproved the al-

97

chemy. Analysis demonstrated that the gold came from the materials used, not the mercury; even the scientists' gold-plated spectacles had contributed. Haber's attitude changed from high enthusiasm to equally passionate scorn. It was a difficult, yet necessary, turnabout.

The gold search had another creative influence. It was helpful in the extraction of bromine and magnesium from solution. The gold research was carefully studied prior to these achievements. Finally Haber came to accept the true worth of the gold study. "If there be no gold," he said, "there will at least be a fine book."

✠

9. The Dahlem Kaiser Wilhelm Institute

✠

AT ITS HEIGHT the Kaiser Wilhelm Society for the Advancement of Science operated thirty-eight research institutes and had more than twelve hundred professional workers including eleven Nobel prize winners. A main center of this pioneer of systematic, scientific research was half an hour from Berlin. Many residents in the vicinity of Dahlem's *Thielplatz* subway station were scientists, along with actress Elisabeth Bergner, known to her scientist neighbors for her Great Dane dogs and Stutz automobile. The men and women who worked in the institutes for chemistry, silicate research, textile chemistry, biology, biochemistry, anthropology and eugenics, metals, physical chemistry, and electrochemistry had pleasant surroundings. Homes and laboratories were embellished with flower gardens, shrubbery, and trees. The workers were also provided with a club, Harnack House, containing large and small halls named after celebrities, a canteen, and a number of bedrooms for visitors. Dahlem workers went there for lunch, meetings, chess, and conversation.

At first the Institute for Physical Chemistry and Electrochemistry had its own lunchroom and cook. This facility was forsaken when Harnack House was built. Haber's institute had two buildings. Besides laboratories and offices, one building housed a constant-temperature room, the machine shop, a lecture hall, the glass-blowing room, library, and living quarters for guests. An enclosed corridor on the ground floor connected to a smaller unit containing offices and laboratories, a high-voltage room, the forge, and a large hall. R. O. Herzog's Institute for Textile Chemistry also occupied the buildings for a number of years after the war.

Haber's institute had taken the desired form during the war. Employees had served through division leaders responsible to Haber. Frederick Kerschbaum, a former pupil of Max Le Blanc, had directed gas-attack problems. Hans Pick had been in charge of gas-defense research. Herbert Freundlich had headed a group also dealing with defense. R. O. Herzog's area had been the gas mask; Ferdinand Flury's province had been pharmacology; Heinrich Weiland had supervised the organic chemistry division. More than 200 chemists and 150 women analysts had worked there.

Haber was intent upon continuing specialist collaboration. He wanted mathematician, physicist, chemist, biologist, and technician to work in unison. Instead of nineteenth-century rugged individualist scientists, he sought twentieth-century co-operators. He was the first to attempt large-scale collaboration in research. Later the biologists in Dahlem followed suit. They succeeded in maintaining an organization comprising leading scientists such as Karl Erich Correns, Max Hartmann, Richard Goldschmidt, and Otto Heinrich Warburg. Today every major research institute in the world is built along these lines. Most university laboratories and all large industrial companies have similar arrangements. Everywhere one-man accomplishments are superseded by those of associated specialists.

In February, 1919, Haber established eight departments in his institute. Physical chemistry was under his super-

Fritz Haber During World War I

SKETCH BY ARNOLD BURSH
COURTESY MRS. MARGARET W. BRUCH

Fritz Haber (far left) *and Richard Willstätter* (center)
in Prague

vision. Physics was led by James Franck, who returned from service as a lieutenant. Collodial chemistry was under Herbert Freundlich, who won the reputation of being a benevolent walking encyclopedia, readily citing references and facts to support a thesis. Organic chemistry, theoretical physics, pharmacology, economic entomology, and textile chemistry were the other departments. For several months Albert Einstein was adviser in theoretical physics, spending a few hours a week at the institute. Fritz Reiche, his successor in this capacity, was consequently sometimes known as "the little oracle."

The organization was maintained for nearly two years. Economic depression and inflation necessitated curtailment of the staff between December, 1920, and March, 1921. Financial support could not be secured despite eloquent appeals for funds by Haber. He believed in the ultimate practical value of scientific research. He claimed Germany could be self-sufficient for thirty-eight million people but food for the twenty million others would have to come through trade of technological superiority for food. Research promoted this superiority.

Physical and colloidal chemistry remained as two departments. When economic conditions improved, physics was reinstated with Rudolph Ladenburg in charge. Michael Polanyi came later to direct work in physical chemistry. In 1926, Haber attempted to secure the services of an outstanding American physical chemist; the man indignantly refused.

Limited funds did not prevent research accomplishment. More than seven hundred publications in scientific journals came from the institute during Haber's tenure. The laboratory work he personally directed was varied, but only a small portion of it was published. Results he never reported concerned cold light, magnetism, the dye malachite green, and the efficiency of benzene as a passageway for electrical current. His published papers dealt with the ultimate architecture of metals, clinging of materials to solid surfaces, the burning of gases, light and heat from chemical reactions, and chain reactions. He studied chain reactions where the end result came after a small number of postulated intermediates, where sensitization with light was required, and where adulterants interfered with the reaction. The ammonia synthesis received very little of his attention. Minor points were clarified; and once an aspirant for the nitrogen-fixation process was rebuked. Both Freundlich and Haber wrote letters to a journal directed against the claims of the author of an elementary chemistry textbook.

Haber gradually became an observer of ammonia synthesis problems. He visited the *Badische* plants infrequently. He had no part in establishing the sales policy for his process. The company had refused foreign offers for patent rights, believing the high-pressure techniques could be kept secret. But once the general principles were known, Georges Claude in France, Luigi Casale in Italy, and engineers in the United States developed similar procedures. Purchase of the finished product from Germany became unnecessary. Earlier, the Belgian Solvay Company, manfacturers of soda ash, had developed a more profitable plan to protect their interests. They had established almost wholly owned subsidiaries in many countries.

Many researchers at the institute credited Haber, often directly in their publications, for some of their accomplishments. Undoubtedly, economic dependency and good manners motivated some of the acknowledgments. But all the scientists would readily agree that Haber provided a refreshing intellectual and scientific atmosphere, with the Monday colloquia furnishing a major portion of this setting.

Colloquia elsewhere meant lectures by research students to the assembled students and co-workers of the professor. The Ostwald colloquia had been held in the Institute for Physical Chemistry in Leipzig; both Herbert Freundlich and Frederick Kerschbaum had taken part in them. They suggested that a similar type of forum be established in Dahlem. Haber was sympathetic to the idea but vetoed student lectures. He was impatient with the hesitation and grasping for words prevalent among aspiring scientists. He wanted specialists who were speakers and teachers.

The Haber colloquium began in October, 1919. Soon it became the outstanding physical chemistry seminar in the area. Others were held at the University of Berlin and the Charlottenburg Engineering College. The physics colloquium organized by Heinrich Rubens and inherited by von Laue was also located in Berlin. Within five years the Haber colloquium was attracting men and women from distant parts of the Republic and a number of foreigners, including Joffé and Funk from Russia. The list of scientists who offered to lecture became lengthy.

Haber often sat in the first row listening attentively. He turned in his seat impatiently awaiting the end when a poor speaker was the attraction. Some poor speakers did appear despite the fact that the program arrangers, Freundlich and Polanyi, always made a serious effort to secure scientists with speaking ability. Haber himself spoke twice. Once he outlined his ideas about oxidation in liquids, giving a detailed chain-reaction mechanism. The second time he analyzed the possibility of powerful forces within liquids, citing his experiments with vanadium pentoxide solutions. Talks of others were never about Haber's achievements or investigations, except for those of an industrial scientist who twice came to discuss the ammonia synthesis.

A broad range of scientific topics was discussed. The seminar was said to cover "everything from the helium atom to the flea." Albrecht Hase was the flea authority. Popular lecturers from other institutes in the Dahlem colony were Otto Warburg, Richard Goldschmidt, and Hermann Mark. Among the Americans who participated were Irving Langmuir, Harry Nicholls Holmes, Edmund Newton Harvey, and Selig Hecht.

Haber was the dominating figure at every meeting he attended. One lecturer confessed that Haber presented a clearer picture in his questions and criticisms than did the lecturer in his talk. Haber's comments after a lecture about the property of certain organisms which emit light without heat showed unusual new research paths. Michael Polanyi said the turning point for one of his theories came when he was invited by Haber to give a talk at a colloquium. Both Einstein and Haber criticized him for his apparent disregard for the scientifically established structure of matter, although some present congratulated him "on the flood of light" he had thrown on the subject. The force of Einstein's and Haber's opinions is shown by Polanyi's claim that, "Professionally, I survived the occasion only by the skin of my teeth."

Haber's comments were infrequently directed toward non-scientific aspects of a talk. He advised indiscriminate use of the masculine, feminine, and neuter definite articles, *der, die,* and *das,* to a foreigner who spoke German poorly. When a dyestuff chemist made dogmatic statements, Haber said, "Here we are accustomed to rely more upon facts than personal assumptions." After an intensely mathematical discourse he would say, "It is all very beautiful but quite above me." The entire assembly would then join him in laughter.

Following one such mathematics session, he blended his comments with autobiography. When at Karlsruhe, he began, he had been a leader in the new science of thermodynamics. His colleagues had come to him for instruction. He had tutored them gladly. However, a professor had protested that he still did not understand, despite the friendly help. Now the lecturer was in the forefront of a new science, and he, Haber, did not understand. He turned and left the room apparently in a huff. But he went immediately to his office and dictated an apology to the speaker. He did make an effort to understand advanced mathematics. He had studied it for six months soon after the war. His remarks and accompanying drama were intended as a plea for simplicity. Many physical chemists and physicists live with equations only. To Haber this was equivalent to stopping at the fence of a house. He wanted to know what was inside. He desired (and most often gained) knowledge of what was behind the equations.

At the end of a talk, Haber might confess, "I do not know whether I understand the problem well, but if you will allow me I will repeat it in a few words." He then would proceed to decipher the discourse with basic concepts. Or he would begin by asking for an explanation of the weak points—to the speaker's chagrin. Sometimes he would begin, "I am an old man," or "I am of an older generation," and with an additional "but" proceed to give his real criticisms. His effectively presented comments directed thinking to new channels, proposed unusual and illuminating analogies, and separated relevant factors. It was a unique combination of clarity, originality, and ability to abstract, spiced with satire and wit.

When the meetings were held at the institute, they were best; standing room only was available. A decrease in quality came with a move to Harnack House. By 1930, the colloquia lost much of their early verve. The principal reason was Haber's frequent absence. Consequently many visitors would telephone before coming to determine whether he would be present.

Scientists were the chief product of the Kaiser Wilhelm Institute for Physical Chemistry and Electrochemistry. Among the men who began careers in Haber's laboratory were R. Ladenburg, K. Bonhoeffer, R. O. Herzog, P. Harteck, C. Zocher, F. Ebert, L. Farkas, H. D. von Schweinitz, F. Flint, P. Goldfinger, and J. Franck. Some later famous scientists remained a very short time: M. Berkmann, J. von Neumann, L. Szilard and E. Wigner. Herbert Freundlich and Michael Polanyi, who became outstanding in their fields, never left Haber's institute.

Haber had simple rules for choosing co-workers and assistants. Intelligence, diligence, and honesty were required. The man was considered, not the job; ability was sought, not reputation. He hired several men despite their having had quarrels with previous employers.

He interviewed one personal assistant for three hours before accepting him. He approached another after noting the quality of his war work. "If you are not in a hurry to obtain a Ph.D.," he began, "I can give you an assistantship. You will be able to write your thesis later using the results of your research." When recruiting for the gold-in-sea-water venture, he took many chemists from his own laboratory. To one he proposed, "You have heard we are starting Department M. I suggest you join. However you must first decide: Do I trust Professor Haber enough to bind my fate to him for several years? Think it over. When it is convenient for you, come and tell me your answer."

The mechanics of Haber's research direction was not a unique molding force, because he followed the customary procedure. His chief assistants would report once or twice a week; he wrote letters to his assistants and left them on their laboratory tables; he would visit the laboratory and chat with all; sometimes one man would trail along to the next, until at the end the entire personnel was listening to him. It was his demands and his treatment of students and assistants that helped make the institute an incubator for young scientists. It was a place where students learned from the master and were inspired by him. As chief and teacher, he encouraged and challenged; as a second father and good friend, he was kind and understanding. He had the ability to develop the potentialities of his men. He had the knack of favorably changing laboratory morale. During a depressing episode in the gold problem, he, within five minutes, had the staff eager and enthusiastic. "Problems without difficulty are not interesting to me," he said. "Almost anyone can do the easy things."

He expected much work from his men. During the weeks of preparation for the first gold-in-sea-water expedition, one assistant invariably took the 1:00 A.M. train home. During the same period, Haber, in his fur-lined coat and top hat, came into the laboratory at midnight to discuss matters with the one or two diligent workers present. Occasionally he would say, "See you at seven or eight," without considering the 5:00 P.M. closing time. Yet no one was ever penalized for not being present after regular hours.

The staff rested a bit when he was away from Dahlem for more than a week. Once he returned unexpectedly, and the institute suddenly became very active. The aroma of his cigar would warn workers of his approach, and a hush of ex-pectation preceded him. Unfortunately, the janitor's cigar had a similar odor and false alarms were plentiful.

Haber always instilled a respect for facts, accuracy, and an understanding of sources of error. A fact was inviolate whether or not it fit into a preconceived curve or idea. Mak-ing excuses for its aberration made him bristle. The labora-tory journal, with its documentary material, was holy.

He expected reports in perfect German. Poor composition irked him as much as faulty speech. On the other hand, he did not expect students to be experts in the language of physical science, mathematics, although he was fond of mathematics and one of his assistants was a frequent house guest for the purpose of carrying out calculations. Once he gave a problem to an assistant who was unable to proceed. "You are not a theoretical soul," said Haber, "but you are a soul. You have a right to refuse work." Later the same man had a mathematical problem to solve, and noticing his inability, Haber gently said, "Let me do it."

He believed science education should be concerned with fundamentals. He thought a young man with a broad back-ground was more apt to bring ideas to new problems than a young specialist. Detailed knowledge, he said, was to be acquired later, with experience. Despite his belief, he was always fearful that industrialists wanted specialists at the start. "I concede that students learn a lot and forget a lot," he said. "I demand a working knowledge of fundamentals." Haber thus believed in the French aphorism, "Everything the child learns in school he forgets—but the education re-mains." Alfred North Whitehead, the early twentieth-cen-tury mathematician and philosopher, said it aptly, "Your learning is useless to you till you have lost your textbooks, burnt your lecture notes, and forgotten the minutae which you learnt by heart for the examination."

In his examination methods, Haber sought to test thinking ability, not memory. He had the habit of beginning with the seemingly far-removed, "Breslau housewives often found brown spots on their washed linen" or "In Hungary, soda ash was pink." Manganese was responsible in both instances, and the student had to review pertinent chemistry. At times Haber would cite a near object and ask questions. The presence of a hat might mean he would start a discussion of felt materials and their treatment; coffee could bring to the fore a discussion on the synthesis of caffeine. The answer, "I don't know," was safe. A guess was dangerous; it could make him furious.

Once he examined a candidate while riding in an automobile from Dahlem to Berlin. After receiving several wrong answers, Haber had the car stopped at a convenient location. "'Look here," he said to the student, "you are dropped now."

On another occasion he asked a candidate for a Doctor of Philosophy degree to state a method for preparing iodine. This element is usually manufactured by chemically treating sea plants, notably kelp. After some hesitation, the student answered, "It is obtained from a tree."

Unruffled, Haber continued, "Iodine tree? Describe one to me." The candidate expanded his guess, telling about height, shape, and type of leaves.

"Where do these trees grow?" asked Haber, not changing expression.

The student, knowing his answers to be imaginative, was cheered by a line of questioning which seemed to indicate their being correct. "In India and Brazil," he replied.

"Where else?" Haber asked immediately.

"The Dutch East Indies," claimed the candidate in full confidence.

"And when do these trees become mature?" continued Haber.

The student was no longer hesitating. "In fifteen years," he said.

"And when do the iodine blossoms appear?" asked Haber.

"In the fall," was the answer.

Then the embarrassed student found a fatherly arm about him, saw a smile of recognition, and heard, "Well, my friend, I will see you again when the iodine blossoms appear once more."

Haber told one doctoral candidate, "I will not examine you about nitrogen fixation. I am so steeped in it that I cannot judge the worth of a student." This was contrary to the practice of other professors, who stressed what they knew.

Haber had the task of quizzing in technology one of his chief assistants in the gold research. (The final examination for the Doctorate of Philosophy degree from the University of Berlin was in chemistry, physics, technology, and philosophy.) "Sit down," he told the scientist one day. "You will take your examination now. If you do badly, no one will know." The assistant wanted to study before the test. "Oh, no," Haber said, "I cannot allow it. You have been my assistant for three years and should know without preparation."

One aspirant for the doctorate could not correctly answer the questions Haber posed and began to cry. Haber called in the man's wife, who was sitting in the outer office. In her presence the man gave excellent replies without tears.

Haber tolerated honest mistakes. When a cold storage plant in Berlin exploded, a worker gave faulty information over the telephone to newspapermen. He said ammonia could not be responsible. Haber's reprimand was the advice,

"When you are not certain of information, look it up. Any elementary textbook will tell you that ammonia forms combustible mixtures with air."

He tried to prevent, as far as he could, the adoption of a laboratory scapegoat. An engineer with the gold-in-seawater project came dangerously close to this status. He was a minority of one among scientists who joked about his use of iron tubes, screws, and valves. Furthermore, the engineer, Ehlermann, had a pathological awe of Haber. One day the laboratory workers left at his work bench half a cigar encased in glass, a few lines of verse, and a note, "Accept, Ehlermann, a cigar. As always, Haber." Haber saw the tableau before it could be completed. To console the man, he sat down and wrote a much better poem, adding, "I am responsible for the spirit of the verse and the quality of the cigar. The engineer is our Lord's cousin. He gives the form to things."

He treated workers as men and equals; he had rapport with them through intellectual and, in some cases, social camaraderie. On board the *Hansa*, he played chess with his assistants and lent them his books. He invited one to use the *Württemberg*'s South Atlantic cruise for a honeymoon trip. "For the jolly time we had in the oxygen-hydrogen explosion," he wrote on a memento to describe research with another. He composed a poem for his chief assistant when crossing the equator. One night he visited the laboratory in dress clothes and made two diligent workers happier by his antics. He sat on the floor and attempted the exercise of placing his knees to his nose. "Help me, gentlemen," he said. "My daughter [born of his second marriage] can do this; I cannot."

He often told his assistants a tale about the most embarrassing moment in his life: When at Karlsruhe he had

owned two frockcoats, and one, used in the laboratory, had
become worn and dirty. He discovered himself at a professional gathering at the Duchess of Baden's wearing the dirty
coat. To add to his discomfort, the royal lady engaged him
in conversation at a moment when his bowels had a sudden urge to move. He experienced great difficulty in observing the amenities and restraining himself at the same time.

He offered a cigar when assistants pleased him and he
was in good humor. He sometimes gave cigars to doctoral
candidates at their oral examinations. He had the cheap, the
moderately priced Graf Bernstoff, and the expensive ones.
When given one of the last, the student was supposed to
smoke it and answer questions at the same time. Occasionally, when pleased with their work, Haber would say, "I'll
get an nice girl to kiss you." Once he chanced upon a promising scientist in a compromising position with a female assistant in the photographic dark room, and both were sum-
marily dismissed.

He would often attend for a few moments the friendly
celebrations for degrees won. He frequently stopped to
watch tennis contests—he had persuaded a leading industrialist to donate two tennis courts to the institute. He used
his own funds when arranging for a specialist's attention
for a female worker suffering from cancer of the brain. She
never knew who her benefactor was, believing that the
money for her operation and care came from institute insur-
ance. He provided, without charge, the services of an outstanding physician for a chemist who had contacted amoebic
dysentery during the last voyage in the gold search. He gave
a stop watch to a student who wanted to purchase it as a
memento. When his secretary asked for time off to attend
the marriage celebration of a departing worker, he told her
the entire staff could go along. The staff of Department M

enjoyed a farewell dinner and garden party at his expense before the first voyage of the *Hansa*. When Niels Bohr visited Dahlem, Haber was pleased to invite the younger men to dine with the renowned scientist.

Finding jobs for his students made him very happy. His policy was merely to harbor youth, because he did not want anyone to grow old in his laboratory. It was a training area, not a place for a career. When one of his assistants received an offer through his own efforts, Haber asked, "Who are these people and why do they want you?" The student replied that it was time to apply what Haber had taught so well. "Well spoken," Haber said, "and 400 marks is also more than 250 marks."

His love for students and assistants was reciprocated. Out of range, however, he was called "the old man" or "the old Fritz," after Frederick the Great. When a visiting foreign scientist had occasion to use Haber's razor to shave, the workers came from all the rooms to question and view this privileged person. At one birthday celebration the laboratory force presented Haber with a model of a ship made with pencils to commemorate the gold voyage—and to give him the pencils he inevitably misplaced. On another occasion many of his cigar butts were collected and placed in a silver box. Only two assistants at the institute had the audacity to talk back to him. One shouted and increased the intensity of his shout, attempting to outdo Haber, while the other whispered and decreased the intensity of his whisper as Haber's tone rose.

10. Personal Relationships

HABER'S RELATIONS with certain colleagues were not always the best; the worst problems occurred with Walther Nernst. Haber's men did not choose to have Nernst as a Ph.D. examiner, especially after Nernst had carefully balanced the publications of one in one hand and had said, "Not so very heavy." On the other side, Haber had examined one outstanding Nernst student, K. F. Bonhoeffer, and later hired him. Nernst and Haber finally came to an understanding near the end of spring, 1933. In the mellowness and wisdom of old age, they had a warm conversation. The antagonism and rivalry which had existed in the past seemed wiped out or regretted.

Karl Bosch, also involved in the nitrogen-fixation achievement, and Haber had amicable but not overly cordial dealings. Followers of the two men created more division than actually existed. When Haber was scheduled to talk at a Heidelberg symposium, the arrangers decided against Bosch as chairman; instead, they asked Haber's friend, George Bredig, to preside.

Haber had minor skirmishes with Karl Correns and Otto Warburg. A representative of the Institute for Advanced Studies in Princeton, New Jersey, asked both Warburg and Haber for advice in selecting a staff. Warburg commented,

"It depends on whether you want scientists or oldsters beyond their prime." Haber, sixty at the time, took this statement as an affront. Upset, he said, "Wait until you are sixty."

He had an argument with an industrial chemist, Carl Duisberg. He referred to the man, privately and to friends, as the King of Leverkusen. (Leverkusen was a plant site of the *Interessen Gemeinschaft Farbenindustrie Aktiengesellschaft*. Originally an association, in 1904, of six principal chemical firms, this became known as *I G*. The *Badische* Company, founded in 1865, was the parent organization. In 1916 two more companies joined; in 1926 eighteen were in the fold.) The conflict arose after the death of the world-renowned organic chemist, Emil Fischer. Fischer, who was obsessed by a fear of death from cancer, had asked Haber what he should use to commit suicide and had received the glib answer, "Cyanide." Fischer used the poison, and Haber felt bad. After Fischer's death Haber and many of his friends urged that Richard Willstätter be given the Fischer post; Willstätter refused it. Haber himself wanted the Fischer professorship in order to be able to examine his own students. Before the war the institute had been host to many unpaid research workers. Afterwards, young men with independent incomes were not plentiful. Haber began to accept students studying for a Doctor of Philosophy degree. These aspiring scholars wanted the assurance of having Haber present during their final examinations. He sought Fischer's professorship for this purpose. Carl Duisberg was the leader of a movement to bar physical chemist Haber from this most coveted chemical professorship in Germany. The opposition was strong, and Haber was finally awarded a professorship of industrial chemistry, and organic chemist Wilhelm Schlenk was named Fischer's successor.

Haber and Schlenk, the latter an accomplished amateur

115

photographer, were close colleagues. Schlenk made a series of camera portraits which showed major moods of Haber. Haber was also on good terms with and an ardent admirer of Albert Einstein; he had met the great physicist through August Marx, a relative of Einstein's. Einstein and Haber became intimate enough for Haber to advise him about divorcing his first wife.

Haber had excellent relations with most scientists in Germany and all foreign naturalists, who chose to forget the poison gas episode. Through a Russian friend, formerly a Karlsruhe student, he became acquainted with the chemist Vladimir M. Ipatieff. When this scientist came to Dahlem for a visit, Haber met him at the subway station on a dark, misty December night and escorted him to his home for dinner. Haber also sent a congratulatory poem on the thirty-fifth anniversary of the scientist's first publication.

With his associates Haber enjoyed many lasting relationships. Herbert Freundlich, known to his assistants as "Uncle Herbert," was always a loyal friend, and Haber's son Hermann did his doctoral research with him. Freundlich served the Institute of Physical Chemistry for twenty years with much liberty in the choice of personnel and handling of problems. Once, when Haber believed that an unpopular worker in Freundlich's laboratory lacked tact and possessed a powerful ambition which would initiate trouble, he wanted to dismiss him, but Freundlich interceded and the man was retained.

Another institute associate director said that true friendship with Haber was impossible because of the continual buzz of his intellectual apparatus. On the other hand, James Franck, for a while an institute department head and a 1925 Nobel prize winner, became a close friend.

Friedrich Epstein was perhaps the most intimate companion from his laboratory. During the war he had served in the War Ministry; through Epstein's diligent efforts, Haber, on the Allied criminal list, had obtained a false passport to escape to Switzerland. Epstein was a Doctor of Philosophy in chemistry and had a wide cultural background. Bald and small in stature, he remained a bachelor, living with his sister and her husband, an art historian, in a fashionable section of Berlin. Epstein had the title of professor and was assigned personnel administration duties at the institute. His work presented at times a dichotomy between him, representing administration, and the other scientists, representing the laboratory worker; this may have been a reason for their caustic references to Epstein's long, manicured fingernails. When Epstein was absent too many days during an illness, Haber became annoyed and expressed his wrath to his son Hermann. Then he cautioned, "If you tell Epstein what I said, I will simply kick you out." In later years Epstein was once accused by an associate director of spending too few hours at the institute and not having scientific interests. Haber defended him, saying that Epstein had performed brilliantly in his doctoral examination.

Haber's secretary, Miss Rita Cracauer, also a War Ministry graduate, was a factotum. Occasionally he introduced her as "my right and left hand." In time, he spoke of her as his adopted daughter. She did such extra work as preparing menus and taking his clothes to the tailor; she had an office in his home as well as in the institute. Once Haber, when he heard that Miss Cracauer's mother, an elderly lady, was ill, stopped all his activities, secured food and wine at a time when both were scarce, and delivered them personally.

Every period of Haber's life had its friendships. They were with varied personalities and with men of widely differing backgrounds, for example, Hans Goldschmidt, a Breslau soap expert, and Max Born, a Nobel prize winner in theoretical physics. No matter the individual, he could discuss personal problems and always come to a solution of the central issue. At times, he provided money, accommodations, and introductions; he sent witty postcards and verse; he enjoyed jocular repartee with each. Foreigner or not, there was reciprocal helpful friendliness. When his son Hermann came to the United States for a visit, Haber asked two of his friends who lived in the East to meet his son at the dock; inadvertently they missed the boat, but that did not preclude proffer of other courtesies to the son of their friend. In Philadelphia, in 1924, newspaper photographers seeking Haber's photograph shoved Fred Carter, his former student at Karlsruhe, out of view. Haber reminded them that they had to include his friend Carter if they wanted his picture.

He had a long and friendly relationship with Max Mayer. After leaving Karlsruhe, Mayer had risen to head a large chemical manufacturing company in Czechoslovakia, *Vereinigte Chemische Farben in Aussig.* In 1925, they jointly purchased a country estate in Württemberg, near Lake Constance. It was an isolated retreat, Ulm being the nearest large city. His and Mayer's houses were about an ordinary street's width apart; each had his own guests. Haber came almost yearly to the farm. Toward the end, however, in December, 1933, when Mayer was in London for a few days, he failed to get in touch with Haber, who was at Cambridge University, to Haber's distress.

Richard Willstätter was another good friend. Four years younger than Haber, he was born in Karlsruhe and was educated at Munich. He became organic chemist Adolph von Baeyer's prize student and successor. He first met Haber on vacation in Zurich during the hot summer of 1911. The two had the common interest of science and many mutual recreations, although Willstätter was staid and polished while Haber was impulsive. In Berlin they went for a walk each evening before retiring; prior to the war they had been especially zealous in this habit. On the Württemberg estate Willstätter was the invariable victor in croquet; since the Munich professor took the game seriously, he was well practiced. In 1930, the two, with some relatives, went for a cruise off the island of Madeira. Here they sent a note to a science journal explaining the sea's blueness—copper was responsible, they wrote. Upon Haber's sixtieth birthday Willstätter presented him with several bottles of wine, vintage 1868, his birth year.

Haber celebrated his sixtieth birthday with a tour up the Nile River accompanied by a number of relatives and friends. Present were Mrs. Haber, Mr. Meffert (widower of the first Mrs. Haber's sister), Haber's sister, Mrs. Freyhan, Haber's son and daughter-in-law, and Friedrich Epstein and Richard Willstätter.

His colleagues at the institute planted an oak tree to commemorate the birthday. A circular stone bearing the inscription "In honor of Fritz Haber" was erected around the tree, with scientists, government officials, and the military present at the ceremonies. The German Bunsen Society sent congratulations to "the versatile and accomplished teacher, the developer of synthetic ammonia, the German who unselfishly gave his all during the war." Scientific journals noted the event, because it was the custom in Germany; on special occasions an entire issue might be devoted to a distinguished scientist's achievements. Paul Askenasy wrote an appreciation for the *Zeitschrift für Angewandte Chemie.* Ernst Berl did the same in *Zeitschrift für Elektrochemie.* The *Biochemisches Zeitschrift* designated their 203d volume as the *Festschrift für Fritz Haber. Die Naturwissen-*

schaften printed commemorative articles by Richard Willstätter, Herbert Freundlich, James Franck, Georg von Hevesy, Otto Stern, Ernst Torres, Robert Le Rossignol, and Margarethe von Wrangell. The last wrote, "Every golden grain
in the fields displays to him the gratitude of the soil he so
richly endowed."

The wife of one of Haber's friends asked her son whether
he, as a child, had liked Uncle Fritz Haber. The boy said
yes, that he was always very kind, then he added, "But we
could not talk to him; we were in awe." The general public
had a similar attitude. One foreign student showed his land-
lord, a four-year war veteran, an autographed photograph
of Haber, and the man immediately called his wife and
daughter and all the neighbors to see what was considered
more or less a marvel—a signed picture of Haber.

Haber also had strong family attachments. He was friendly even with some persons related by marriage—he was a
good friend of the husband of his first wife's sister, Meffert,
a widower and patent attorney. Haber was noticeably upset
when the child of his second wife's sister died. One first
cousin, an attorney, had been an early schoolmate but had
died in the war; Haber was attached to the widow and
aided her and the children, two sons and a daughter. When
one son emigrated to South America, he gave him one thousand dollars and letters of introduction to Argentine bankers.
He took the time to write the young man thoughtful letters
of encouragement and advice; however, when asked for five
thousand dollars more, Haber reprimanded, "Don't tell me
how to lose my money." The young man at one time asked
him whether he was searching for an investment for income
for his retirement years, and Haber was offended. "My boy,"
he said, "don't you think you are indiscreet? There is criticism in your query. Be more careful." The young man's sis-

ter did not fare as well. After she made a remark which offended him, he advised her not to visit again.

He was close to the two granddaughters of his favorite uncle, Hermann; their mother was named after his mother. One granddaughter became a laboratory assistant and secretary at his institute; for a time the other was his housekeeper. The elder, Elizabeth Freund, once received vocational guidance from him. He told her that since she had not stained her hands, spotted her aprons, or worked in the kitchen of her home, she should not study chemistry. At his suggestion, she traced the Haber genealogy and found Fritz Haber to be the only genius in the family. He was a helpful brother to his three stepsisters and their families. Frieda's husband, Glücksmann, was in the real estate business; Helene Weigert and Else Freyhan were married to physicians. He rewarded his nephew Dieter Freyhan for every new slang expression reported; he had discussions about politics with nephew Robert Freyhan; he entertained with spontaneously composed rhymes at his nephew Karl Weigert's confirmation. In later years, he advised this young physicist to reject an offer of employment from the university at Istanbul, because of its poor financial condition. He was closest to the eldest of his sisters, Else; and when her husband died in 1930, she came to live with Haber. In an intimate circle he could concoct fantastic, funny stories upon themes which involved her.

Fritz Haber's son Hermann was like his father in many respects, including his penchant for composing impromptu verse. Hermann did not want to become a scientist; he preferred being an attorney. But father and son compromised, and Hermann became a patent attorney. Haber objected to his son's marriage at an early age. The son's choice of a wife (the former Margaret Stern) was not the cause of the opposition; on the contrary, she became much of a favorite. She helped Haber with his secretarial work when Hermann Haber and his family lived in his father's house. Fritz Haber liked the Stern family, old Breslau residents. His daughter-in-law's brother, Dr. Rudolf Stern, a physician, worked in his institute for a while; he also spent five vacation weeks with him at Monte Carlo. Dr. Stern and his wife, Katherine, were frequent guests at Haber's country estate. There Katherine wrote, and others read and discussed, a book manuscript about child training. She and Richard Willstätter's daughter, Margaret, were his "adopted" nieces; both called him "uncle." Mrs. Rudolf Stern was the daughter of the Breslau pathology professor Breger. At times Mrs. Breger came to the farm accompanied by her son. He and Robert Freyhan were interested in art and art history and found enlightened conversation with Fritz Haber.

Haber was an affectionate grandfather to Hermann's two daughters. He addressed them by the pet names of "Schnugi" and "Putzi" and played dominoes with the elder. Once they and their mother occupied an institute guest room across the hall from Margaret Willstätter. Haber also had two small children of his own, a daughter, Eva, born in 1918, and a son, Ludwig, three years younger. His divorce from their mother, however, precluded a really close relationship with them.

When first married, Charlotta Haber did her utmost to respect her husband's interests and provide companionship for him. For about a year she succeeded in the almost impossible task of being a great intellectual's wife. She was a pleasant helpmate, friendly to all his guests and never retiring or embarrassed—even when pregnant. But the time came when Haber would publicly berate his wife when irritated by a remark or a mannerism of hers. Then one or the other would have a tantrum, and a full-scale row was under way. It usually ended by his writing her some verse and thus effecting a reconciliation—for a while.

These public insults, however, were not all of Charlotta's grievances. Another was Haber's habitual lateness for dinner. When he didn't appear on time, she would call the institute, and he would be too busy to answer. After a number of calls, he would instruct an assistant, "Tell her I'm not here." By the end of 1925, the disagreement between Haber and his wife intensified. One argument followed another without many intervening days of calm. When the misunderstanding was most acute, Haber sought the assistance of Friedrich Epstein in composing letters of reconciliation; but all success was only temporary.

Basically Haber was considerate, spirited, and a romanticist, but he was too much the hard-working thinker, too much the objective scientist, and too easily annoyed to be an appreciative or appreciated husband. Moreover, he had a conception of a perfect mate for a scientist. He thought the wife of skin specialist Albert Neisser, an old friend from the Breslau Academic Literary Society, was close to the ideal.

Mrs. Haber, of a younger generation, had different standards. Attending a social function with a man other than her husband was accepted in her circle. Fritz, on the other hand, was affronted by her occasional visits to night clubs or extended visits out of the city. Her interests, ideas, and desires were simply different from his. She enjoyed dancing; he despised it. She liked cabarets; he avoided them. Travel was their only mutually enjoyed diversion.

Charlotta believed young Hermann partly responsible for the marital difficulties. She had the problem of acquiring a stepson almost her own age; Hermann had an equally arduous task of adjustment. Fortunately, he was away from Dahlem most of the time during the ten-year marriage.

Fritz Haber toyed with the idea of separation during the summer of 1926. He was annoyed by an unexpected long absence of his wife. He went to his friend Willstätter's house in Munich to think about the situation. He decided to try a period of separation, but his idea, after discussion with his wife, resulted in divorce instead in the autumn of 1927. The two remained friends; in fact, in 1928, Charlotta accompanied him on the Nile River excursion. Then in 1930 a passionate love seemed rekindled, but this time finances intervened. He asked for a new divorce settlement in order to help meet the demands of his creditors. Charlotta and the children were receiving one-sixth of his income. She voluntarily gave up her automobile allowance, but when he requested other economies, she rebelled and sought legal advice. Her alimony was finally reduced to one-third of the original amount.

Haber always enjoyed and sought the company of women. Disinterested observers believed that the opposite sex did not have to be too clever to sustain his attention. Women had only to know how to distract him or how to listen. Once a lady monopolized his time with her words, and he said of her, "She rippled along so agreeably." He sensed his deficiencies for romance. In 1930 he sadly told the wife of a good friend that women to him were like butterflies—beautiful to look at, but if he tried to touch them, only the colorful dust remained in his hand.

II. Understanding the Man Haber

FRITZ HABER once claimed that he was really shy, but this characteristic was not noticeable. Neither was a feeling of inadequacy prominent, though he did show many symptoms of insecurity. For one, he always kept large amounts of currency on his person. He carried the entire funds for the expenses of the 1928 Nile trip in paper and silver. He was found in his stateroom at the port of embarkation, Genoa, Italy, taking money from all his pockets and making a pile on the bed; he had $10,000 in Swiss, German, Italian, and Egyptian currency.

Like a homesick traveler, he befriended people from Breslau and Silesia. Both his wives were from the territory. His secretary's parents, Max Born's wife, K. F. Bonhoeffer, Franz Goldschmidt, Paul Askenasy, Georg Lunge, Dr. Rudolf Stern, his wartime valet, and others were born in the region. With eagerness, he served the larger entity than himself, Germany. He reaffirmed Johann Fichte's "To be German is to have character." Probably he would have subscribed to an 1848 revolutionist slogan, "The salvation of the world will come from Germany." His patriotism was a devotion, not a loyalty; a self-sacrifice rather than a duty; a deep-rooted faith rather than an inculcated creed. An index of his passion to belong was his self-association with the German literary great. He spoke the language of Goethe and Schiller without a Silesian accent. His sentences were thus filled with unusual comparisons and parallels. He was proud of his word mastery and demanded that students acquire the same. One evening an assistant's and his dinner became cold while he found and read a fine speech that had been delivered at Beethoven's death; he had been displeased with a eulogy heard that day.

His working at a variety of endeavors was another indication of his search for identity. He completed investigations in every major division of chemistry; he was a scientist, administrator, soldier, economist, and poet. He first wife said that were he not a genius as a chemist, he would have been one as a merchant. He had talents as an author and diplomat. If he had been an Englishman, he might have been Viceroy of India; as an American he would have been a top industrial executive.

He had extraordinary and recognized abilities as an organizer and co-ordinator. He first demonstated these at Karlsruhe, and then throughout 1914–18. Indeed, he was happiest during the war, directing large numbers of workers and associating with influential men. His institute at Dahlem became the greatest of its kind in the world; when laymen thought of the Kaiser Wilhelm Institutes, they thought of Haber.

He had a wide panorama of interests. He could speak intelligently not only about science but also about economics, politics, and human affairs. He knew and entertained artists; although he was not a music lover, he was a friend of Siegfried Ochs, founder and conductor of the Berlin Philharmonic Orchestra.

He had a knack for showmanship. He had the theatrical sense, the flare for intelligent exhibitionism and the colorful behavior displayed by many men of affairs. Some of this came from training. During his student days dramatics was the extracurricular activity that had most intrigued him; one of his diversions at Karlsruhe had been the theater, which he thoroughly enjoyed. Some of the talent could have been developed as a kind of unconscious imitation of Hans Bunte of Karlsruhe; students of his similarily acquired some of his modes of behavior. Perhaps a portion of his Thespian adroitness stemmed from insecurity compensation patterns.

When head of the Chemical Warfare Service, he once came late to a scheduled meeting of officers and entered panting to demonstrate, to the displeasure of the military, his late arrival. It was more natural for him to act out an excuse than simply to state regrets. He also occasionally acted out his humor. He had a standard procedure for calling a meeting to order at the *Metallgesellschaft* in Frankfurt by pounding the table with a closed fist and saying, "Gentlemen, when *Geheimrat* Professor Haber is at the head of the table, everyone must keep his trap shut."

He more or less adopted new roles on the stage of life. Following a trip to the Orient, he paraded before guests in a Japanese kimona. During the war he had been ambitious for a general staff officer's uniform having a broad red stripe down the trousers' sides.

He played the role of Disraeli, nineteenth-century prime minister of England, a Jew who devoted himself to England, with masterly expression and adroit maneuvers. On a trip to the Near East, Disraeli, Lord Beaconsfield, at times wore "red cap, red slippers, broad blue striped jacket and trousers." As Disraeli's maiden speech in the House of Commons was unsuccessful, so Haber's first research in chemistry did not bear fruit.

Haber also played the role of nineteenth-century scientist

Paul Ehrlich, also from Breslau, a cigar smoker, avid drinker of mineral water, and reader of mystery stories. Haber's experiments, like Ehrlich's, had romantic overtones at times.

He played the role of Wilhelm II, born with a stunted arm, alternately spoiled and overdisciplined. Theatrical, vain, self-righteous, and ambitious, Wilhelm II had quarreled with his parents; when his father Wilhelm I died of cancer, Wilhelm II behaved like a cad. Wilhelm II paraded in flamboyant uniforms. He enjoyed watching the chief of his military cabinet dress up as a ballerina and dance before the court. His signature was on Haber's appointment paper, and a framed letter from the Kaiser authorizing initiation of gas warfare was in Haber's Dahlem study. On the basis of a short talk with Wilhelm, Haber judged him to be a man who would have been a brilliant journalist, Wilhelm was interested in many things and was quick to understand exterior aspects; he knew how to dramatize a situation and quickly forget it.

Perhaps insecurity was responsible for Haber's tremendous drive to work. Along with other prominent scholars of every age, he was constantly working; he virtually lost himself in his duties and projects. On many nights he was busy until 2:00 or 3:00 A.M. Piles of books were always about his night table. Even at his country estate, he reserved a few morning hours for work. He did say "work is the refuge of people who suffer materially and spiritually." Unfortunately, he expected others to have the same unremitting industry; he severely taxed the energy of almost everyone around him.

His lack of sense of time was a result of his absorption in work. He sometimes left memoranda to his assistants on Saturdays and Sundays. He had many five-hour meetings with them. If an idea interested him, he stayed with it, missing appointments. An evening's discussion could last until early morning if someone did not suggest adjournment. An American scientist visiting Berlin made arrangements to see Nobel prize winner Max von Laue at 6:00 P.M. on a certain day. When he told von Laue that he was to see Haber at 4:00 P.M. the same day, Laue suggested that the American come at 7:30 or 8:00; the American arrived at von Laue's home at 9:00.

Perhaps Haber's vanity and sensitivity came from a latent desire to bolster himself and his place in society. He was easily offended; the slightest provocation stirred him. He responded quickly to any misinterpretation or slighting of his scientific work. At Karlsruhe in 1900 he wrote a letter of rebuttal to a scientific journal carrying a criticism of the chief chemist of the Magdeburg Gas and Water Works. At Dahlem, an enterprising young assistant once pointed out a mistake in grammar that Haber had made; Haber did not speak to him the remainder of the day. A student speaking at the colloquium about the survey of his own experimental results failed to mention Haber's contribution to the problem. Although previously cautioned about assigning credit, he was so nervous he forgot to make acknowledgments. The minor omission upset Haber; he stormed at the innocent student and demanded an explanation; he scolded the young man's sponsor. However, after a few days had elapsed, Haber said he was sorry for his attitude.

He did have a low boiling point. When some institute laboratory apparatus was stolen, he prepared to call the police. The assistant who reported the theft cautioned against the move by holding Haber's hand against the telephone. Haber was furious and demanded to know who was the boss in his institute. But the next day he apologized to the assistant. One day in 1922 an American student happened to be searching for a book in the institute library when Haber entered. Not knowing Haber or the German custom of a subordinate's greeting his superior first, the student failed to say "Good morning" or nod his head. Angry, Haber approached him and said, "I am accustomed to a greeting in my library." The embarrassed student confessed his ignorance of the custom and offered apologies. He was informed in a deep and clear voice, "*Mein Namen ist Haber.*"

Haber's insecurity may have stemmed from his early background. The youthful failures, that almost all successful men have when climbing the ladder toward acceptance, probably weighed more heavily upon him than upon most. A converted Jew, he had the problem of negating the past even though not rooted in Judaism. His innermost feelings should have been similar to those of the German princes. Both Jews and royalty needed to realize that they were a marked minority in the German nation—a nation in which they were not entirely wanted. At the same time, both felt that they were deserving. The death of Haber's mother at his birth left an indelible scar, as did the deaths of others—his first wife and Emil Fischer for example. He also felt deeply the deaths resulting from the cholera epidemic in Hamburg, poison gas, and the manufacture of explosives through the ammonia synthesis. True, his accomplishments were also used for maintaining and safeguarding life, as in the coal-gas detector and the production of fertilizers. But he was ever sensitive to the less humane aspects of the results of his work. His sensitivity carried into all phases of his life. One of his men at the institute introduced his wife and child to Haber. The boy in awe hid behind his mother. Haber in a mildly reprimanding tone asked, "Why do you look at me like that, my child? I am not a villain."

He was continually striving to reach again the scientific

heights attained when he first gained international recognition. Something as amazing and spectacular as nitrogen fixation had his instant attention. Perhaps he wanted an unquestioned repeat performance to ensure his place in science. He regretted not having a great general law of science to his credit. He had come close to the achievement, within recognizable distance of Nernst's heat theorem.

Haber received many honorary awards. He was elected president of the German Chemical Society in 1923; received an honorary Doctor of Agriculture degree from the Berlin Agricultural School, the Wilhelm Eimer Medal of the Lower Austrian Business Society, and the coveted Goethe Medal awarded by the president; he was made advisory editor of the *Biochemisches Zeitschrift* and was a member of the editorial board of the *Zeitschrift für Elektrochemie*. Still, he was ambitious for greater achievement and some degree of control wherever he was involved.

His associates cautioned him to rest more. They would say that he had done enough for one man and that his health would suffer, but he had no patience with such advice. Urged to take a vacation, he would ask where else would he find the comforts of his home; on vacation he would do the work of his chauffeur and maid.

Unfortunately he considered his body an organism for keeping his mind in proper working order. He never realized that it could limit mental activity. He viewed its deficiencies as another man would look upon a silly fool who came to disturb him. He suffered a mixture of surprise and annoyance when his body, which had served faithfully for so many years, suddenly became impertinent enough to impose limitations. At fifty, he felt the first disturbances; at sixty, they became severe. In 1911 he suffered from gallstones. After the war he was plagued with a disorder resembling *diabetes insipidus,* as has been related. Some of his physicians believed the disease was functional. Drinking great quantities of mineral water gave him a measure of relief; a special diet helped. In 1927, angina pectoris became acute, and he began to carry a small bottle of nitroglycerine along with a silver spoon. August scientific assemblies were sometimes the witnesses to the drug taking. In mild attacks he held his thumb under his chin at the neck junction. He became pale or greenish during an angina seizure and would hold tightly to a stable object. Since the intense pain lasted only a moment, he would catch his breath and continue his sentence. Once a young chemist, ambitious to join the Berlin University faculty, had tea with him. They had a slight argument about a chemical reaction, and Haber suffered a mild attack. The young man expressed fear to his companion and sponsor, an institute assistant, that Haber might die as a result of this provocation. He did manage to make others believe he was severely ill. He gulped many glasses of water, took more nitroglycerine than was necessary, and was always short of breath. He was a depressing sight when hardening of the arteries and insomnia also set in; occasionally he took pills to counteract the sleeplessness. Once he asked a visiting second cousin to aid him in going up the stairs of his home: "Do your old uncle a favor. Put your hand on my back." This permitted him to ascend leaning backwards and so to breathe easier. An acquaintance once asked him the reason for the thumb-to-neck habit. Haber exaggerated and said he had a peculiar electrical body condition. One associate privately implied that Haber's illness was in large measure hysteria.

Perhaps Haber was afraid of deteriorating mentally with old age. To children he would say, "I'm an old man; I'm not going to live." Walking with a cane, he greeted Harold

Hartley, one-time chief of chemical warfare, with, "I am an old man." When escorting Margarethe von Wrangell (Princess Andronikow through marriage to a Russian prince) up institute stairs, he said to Freundlich, "Ah, my dear colleague, help an old man and our friend, a princess." In 1929 his personal assistants had a gay time during the two days before Lent. The next morning, dissatisfied with their sleeplessness and mood, Haber said, "Now, boys, you have to admit that an old codger like myself may be losing his mind. But give me some credit."

Haber's normal approach to people was characterized by the wisdom of a man of experience coupled with native kindness and understanding. He gave high priority to aiding those who needed assistance. He encouraged them, he gave them money, he advised in detail. One woman friend concluded that he was frequently more kind than clever, however superior his brain power. He wrote scores of letters of recommendation. He built the careers of many of his students step by step. If a situation was too complex for advice, he appeared as tormented as if he were personally involved. He did favors for people whether asked or not. Once he said to a friend, "How is it you have never asked me for anything?"

His philanthrophy was not limited to friends, relatives, associates, and students; basically he had a warm feeling for almost everybody. He made almost pitiful attempts at deference in conversing with the provincial bailiff near his country home. With the air of a chivalrous knight he would remove his hat and bow low when passing peasant women; he also made a deep bow to the woman who scrubbed the floors at the institute. Upon leaving a home in Karlsbad where he had been a guest, he shook hands with all the servants—gardener, chauffeur, cook, and maid. These gestures did not appear premeditated. He seemed to be aware of human dignity even when dealing with the less-educated, less-talented, and more unfortunate members of society. When he visited his friend Willstätter, he told entertaining stories to the housekeeper, Miss Hofmann; and when he wrote his friend, he invariably added, "Regards to Miss Hofmann." Once he and Willstätter excitedly called the woman to look at the color of the water in a bathtub; he gave a physical explanation and Willstätter a chemical one.

When Princess Andronikow visited his country estate, he cautioned everyone to address her with the title, "Your Highness." He walked alongside an Agfa Anilin director who was riding horseback, not to kow-tow but as a sign of respect. He also tried to put at ease those who had not yet made their reputations. When a young assistant of Max Born's was introduced to him, he joked in a friendly way with the awe-stricken student. "Did you study my books? Did you sweat over them?" he laughed. When he and Willstätter on an Adriatic vacation arrived late in an overcrowded railroad dining car, he joked with the waiter about the long wait for service by commenting, "Could you bring me a coffin?" and "How much is a cemetery lot in Dubrovnik?" He did not say he was the famous Haber. Haber used his position and titles to vie with equals or advance his friends and associates. He knew the value of titles, however, even in republican Germany. He was addressed as *Herr Geheimrat*. Originally equivalent to privy councilor, the title came to signify importance to the community. Men could receive the honor of this title on attaining a full professorship.

A dropped suitcase tore a hole in the trousers of an assistant on a train to Hamburg. With pompous dignity Haber, on this occasion, chose to use position in addressing the owner of the case, who was a Finnish diplomat en route to Helsinki. Haber threatened to speak to his friends in the Foreign Office. The Finn then indicated a willingness to pay for the damage, fearing his government would not. Haber handed the conductor a card useful for such occasions. It was inscribed "Professor, Dr. Phil., Dr. Ing., E. H., Dr. d. Landw., E. H., Fritz Haber, Nobel Prize winner, former Director of the German Chemical Warfare Service, Director of the Kaiser Wilhelm Institute for Physical Chemistry and Electrochemistry." He had another calling card, used on friendlier occasions, which read just "Fritz Haber." The railroad could be held liable for negligence, he told the impressed trainman, because the stop might have been too sudden, and he ordered him to measure the width of the baggage holder. Then Haber advised his assistant, "You are on an official trip. You will not pay for the trousers."

He was adept in the practices of German society because many of the formalities were fun for him. He successfully carried his nineteenth-century regal manners into the twentieth century. He also adjusted well to professorial social life. He enjoyed courtesy calls on and entertainment of colleagues. He also invited artists, writers, scientists, businessmen, and diplomats to his sumptuous home. A congenial host, he moved from one small group to another. At one gathering all the guests came in formal wear save Albert Einstein. After a dinner party for Niels Bohr, Haber's second cousin remarked that one of the young physicists was an excellent dancer, and Haber took exception to the statement. "Either a man is a good physicist or a good dancer," he said. "The same individual cannot be both."

He invited a former student to dinner, and the man arrived to find Haber and his wife in the middle of the meal. Haber had forgotten the engagement. Mrs. Haber said to the visitor, "Don't you know that you have to confirm ap-

pointments with me?" Haber jested to his wife, "Now you
will have to wish something on the table."

He had the proverbial professorial absent-mindedness.
On board the *Württemberg*, the Captain finally tied all pencils to immovable objects because Haber was constantly taking and misplacing them. His secretary would give him half
a box of matches so that he would not lose all of them at
one time. She also kept track of his felt hat even when Herbert Freundlich was present with his—a hasty glance at the
initials on the lining could confuse the initials H. F. and F. H.
One assistant, working with cyanide solution, devoted about
half of his attention to Haber's suggestions and the other half
to making sure that the professor didn't inadvertently dip
his cigar into the poison and then put it back in his mouth.
Once a long search was conducted at the institute for Haber's false teeth. They were found doing service as a book-
mark in *Beilstein,* the reference volume for organic chemists.

One Saturday afternoon when he was working with an
assistant, Haber suddenly remembered a Berlin engagement
and hurriedly went to shave. In a moment he came out of
the bathroom bloody and lamenting, "What can I do? I
cannot go now." The assistant volunteered his help and
shaved his grateful professor. "I will help you with your
work," promised Haber in return.

The simple procedures of everyday living seemed difficult for the man of science. Dressing to attend the unveil-
ing of a bust at the Prussian Academy of Science, he called
upon a cousin for aid in adjusting his necktie. He had already
soiled his coat. At Karlsruhe he was often without a necktie or wore one that was little more than a string. He generally wore sack suits and was well dressed only for special
occasions. At a meeting of the German Chemical Society in

Leipzig in 1922, he attended a hot afternoon session wearing a winter coat. Ties invariably gave him trouble—his friend Willstätter had to tie his bow tie for him when they were vacationing together and formal dress was necessary.

Haber appeared to be an extraordinary but not happy man. After the war he defined happiness as a sense of well-being and buoyancy. In 1927 happiness to him meant acquiring a special richness of life through a deep love or the satisfaction of working for the betterment of humanity. When he was ill, he confessed, "I am beyond all this and I cannot feel happiness any more."

Fritz Haber read many books and articles dealing with science, although in later years he assigned long journal papers to his assistants for abstracting. He was an almost equally avid reader in fields outside of science. He particularly enjoyed Goethe's works and André Maurois' books about Colonel Bramble. He was familiar enough with the Bible to quote from it; he and Willstätter planned a vacation after a discussion of biblical passages. He was passionately fond of detective stories, especially about Nick Carter or by Edgar Wallace. He had a detective story in his pocket almost always. During his ten days in the eastern United States in 1923, an American friend pleased him by presenting him with several thrillers. Once he asked the return of a few such volumes which he had given a sick friend; he could not bear not to have them in his library. Rereading familiar tales often helped his insomnia. He noted at the edge of a galley proof of one of his articles which he sent to Willstätter, "It is better to read a mystery." The thrillers probably affected his outlook in other areas. Soon after the war, in answering an English criticism of his poison-gas work, he wrote, "It is always dangerous to attempt to form a correct estimate of the intentions of others from the traces of events they have left behind them." He thus aligned himself with the cautious type of detective.

Haber's own literary efforts were directed to verse. He composed, most often in hexameters, appreciations or congratulatory poems for friends and colleagues. When his Harch automobile proved faulty the third time used, he wrote a poem rather than a letter of complaint (he was on the company board of directors). When speaking at such functions as the fiftieth anniversary of the Academic Literary Society of the University of Breslau, in June, 1924, he would read one of his verses. When giving presents, such as the copy of Thomas Carlyle's *French Revolution* which he gave a friend, he added poetry. At Karlsruhe, he often asked the stockroom clerk for apparatus in rhyme. During a social evening he could converse in couplets for a few hours and was pleased if someone followed suit. His daughter-in-law memorized some of this impromptu verse. He knew, too, the poetry of the masters; in his generation educated men memorized masterpieces of literature. Emil Fischer and Richard Willstätter, among others, could recite long passages from the classics. Haber carried this to the extreme, and it showed in his conversation.

He had a strong, sharp, piercing voice that became deeper after 1930. He spoke slowly and hesitatingly, searching for the best expression, emphasizing his words, and breathing heavily through his nose. At times he would be finishing one thought while his companion was anticipating the next. His conversation was like a friendly sermon or speech, with an air of majesty; Nobel prize winner and physicist Gustav Hertz imitated him well.

Haber would pace up and down when holding a discussion. The halls of the institute and his garden were admirable for this purpose; home and office rooms were too small. There was an enclosed corridor between the two buildings of the institute and a long, covered way in the garden. He received visitors in both places, which came to be known as "the scientific runways."

Usually Haber did the talking in company because he excelled in ideas and conversation, but he was attentive if someone else had interesting ideas. Sometimes he claimed to be hard of hearing when he did not choose to listen. Good friends could nonetheless alert him with a teasing whisper. He spoke casually to them and to his secretary only in leisure moments.

Talking to him was an intellectual strain for the learned as well as for his students. He was a searching conversationalist, never allowing an empty phrase or a vague expression to pass. He was dissatisfied with superficial knowledge and sought basic facts and ideas. One of his physicians found prescription writing difficult because Haber wanted to know all the physiology and pharmacology involved; he would quiz the doctor until the latter became almost ill. He did like to draw people out, particularly the shy. He did so not with the thought of influencing others by discussing their interests, but in search of new ideas.

Although he was not given to small talk, yet he had his own brand of inconsequential subjects. An excellent raconteur, he could weave fantastic tales with little effort. His great fund of travel and scientific experiences provided a good background for fantasy; he was a sought-after storyteller. Always he created his imaginative romances with someone he knew as the central character. He once regaled Willstätter's housekeeper with the adventures of her lost hat. He involved his wife in his so-called pilgrimage to Mecca; she was supposed to have letters to prove his journey. He pointed out a piece of sculpture by his sister, Mrs. Glücksmann, as the bust of the janitor at Karlsruhe; he needed no prompting to repeat the tale of the drunken porter's sponsoring him into the academic world.

He made stirring public addresses before the chemists of Heidelberg, August 3, 1908; the Science Society of Karlsruhe, March 18, 1910; and the Society of German Chemists, Bonn-on-the-Rhine, June 3, 1914. His pointed comments at a meeting of the Bunsen Society in Leipzig during the spring of 1914 jolted the slow-moving proceedings of an afternoon session into an active discussion. At one gathering another notable's blunder clouded the atmosphere; Haber's fine speech cleared the air. He displayed admirable diplomacy at the wedding reception of a secretary to Freundlich. She had been inefficient, so he carefully quoted compliments of others and did not add anything of his own.

One of his most appreciated speeches was extemporaneous and never printed. In the autumn of 1920, James Franck, still in his thirties, was invited to join the faculty of Göttingen University. This was indeed an honor. An array of famous scientists had worked there. Mathematicians Karl Gauss, Georg Riemann, and Hermann Minkowski, physicist Wilhelm Weber, and chemist Friedrich Wöhler had been among the foremost. At a farewell dinner for Franck before he left the institute, Haber began, "It was in the year 1890 that I was sitting with my friend Abegg and I envied him. I envied Abegg first because he was going to Göttingen as an assistant and second because he had become an officer in the reserve. For these two things I envied Abegg enormously. And now Franck goes to Göttingen." For fifteen minutes Haber held his audience to an attention most of them never again duplicated. "There are three stages in the development of academic life," he said, "to become, to be, and to represent." He complimented young Franck with, "May the representing be easy for you."

Most of his addresses were prepared in advance. He would begin dictating about two days beforehand and the completed document would go into his pocket; yet on several occasions he delivered an entirely different talk. He dictated many of his scientific writings while pacing the floor of his office. Revisions were seldom necessary because he had a knack for phrasing properly from the beginning. He believed that self-disciplined training was responsible for this ability. However, he was not so skilled in drawing, and his quick sketches of apparatus needed study to be deciphered.

His speech to the Reichstag in 1919 seemed to appeal to all present. He spoke exceptionally well in 1922 on the eightieth birthday of his Karlsruhe colleague, Karl Engler. When appraising the qualities of his friend and teacher, Georg Lunge, in a 1923 eulogy, he said, "His scientific work conquered provinces in which previously only the crafts undertook expeditions." In speaking of Niels Bohr, he said, "They [men like Bohr] are like the great prophets of the Bible. They see things with extraordinary vision beyond the reach of ordinary mortals. They are the seers who have great flashes of inspiration." To him and to many others, Bohr's application of the quantum theory to the hydrogen atom was a work of superb genius ranking with the great accomplishments of science.

At Adolf von Harnack's seventy-fifth birthday celebration in 1926, Haber said, "The last quarter of a century has been a great time for scientific research despite wars and human misery. The researches of the nineteenth century were like oases in the desert. The last quarter-century has shown these oases can be united." In 1929 he asked a visiting American whether he found the research institutes of the

Kaiser Wilhelm Society an ornament to German culture, adding that the institutes were not a decoration but a necessity. Germany could be self-sufficient for thirty-eight million people; the other twenty million depended upon food from abroad, and research would make these less dependent.

In July, 1928, the Liebig-Wöhler celebrations were held at Darmstadt and Giessen to honor the nineteenth-century Germans who had established organic chemistry. Justus Liebig's birthplace was restored and dedicated, and Eugene Spiro's portrait of Haber was placed in the house. Said Haber of Liebig, "I know of none among the warriors of our science, yes, in the entire realm of natural science, who received more grateful love during his life and who had greater love follow him into enternity." Like Haber, Liebig had been largely self-taught, regardless of the number of universities attended. Like other famous men, he had his favorite bon mots, such as, "Young people are not receptacles to be filled; they are fires to be kindled." Like Haber, he had been equally outstanding as a theoretical and an industrial chemist. Like Haber, Liebig had an outstanding accomplishment in agricultural chemistry, having been the first to emphasize the importance of artificial fertilizers. Like Haber, Liebig had been an impressive personality, an excellent speaker, and a cosmopolite. "We ask before we take leave of him," said Haber, "having said so much of his strength of will and mind, how was it with his soul? For no one deserves to be counted among the immortals—no matter how great his power and inspired his mind—if he lacks greatness of soul. All who knew him say of him that he was true from the bottom of his heart, upright and good, yet proud and of high thoughts."

Eighteen of Haber's public speeches were published in

two volumes. The first volume, issued in 1924, containing five addresses and a dedication to Richard Willstätter, was entitled *Fünf Vorträge aus den Jähren, 1920–23.* The second, appearing in 1928, was *Aus Leben und Beruf: Ausätze, Reden, Vorträge.* It was reviewed as "a book of extraordinary interest to German patriots" by "a brilliant speaker" who uses "thoroughly clear logic" and makes "well-defined points."

Speaking and writing were an avenue for sharing some of his ideas—one acquaintance said he was always full of inspiring and brilliant thoughts. But his patterns of thought were equally valuable. Essentially, he used an uncommon common sense first and then, if necessary, his wide and specialized knowledge. He had a marked ability to see essences. He sifted details, not taking anything for granted, and came to the solution or the core of a difficulty; he could detect flaws in data.

He approached problems with energy, vigor, and confidence. He had great optimism about the possibilities of overcoming all barriers. As he became engrossed in a problem his enthusiasm rose, often entirely out of proportion to the importance of the undertaking. Even in his advanced years he showed the same fervent zeal for scientific problems generally found among the younger generation.

He demanded and loved work requiring him to think. When finished with a task, he would immediately seek other, comparable pursuits. He could not sit idle throughout the twenty-five-minute drive from Dahlem to Berlin; he worked and conversed. On vacation, he would go for a walk only to think; when he was through reasoning, he would return. In Switzerland, on mountain jaunts, he was always asking questions and developing opinions about minutia as well as matters of importance. His companions soon lost their breath in what became the adjunct activity of climbing. He scolded relatives if occasionally their conversation in his house drifted from a high plane. He preferred intellectual parlor games as part of the evening's entertainment at his country estate.

Willstätter, the friend who knew both his weaknesses and his strengths, in whose company he was most at ease, said of Haber in 1928: He had "breadth of vision, depth of thought and perception, love of new and often unconquerable kingdoms of thought, wealth of ideas and of verbal expression, warmth of feeling." Haber's "greatness lay in the conception of ideas of a scientific nature. The stimulation, the plan, the method were more important to him than the result. Creative work pleased him more than the completed task."

✠

12. International Acclaim

✠

FRITZ HABER had many contacts with foreigners, principally because his laboratory attracted them. In 1929, at least half of the sixty staff members, guests or permanently employed, were not citizens of the Republic; his personal assistants were a Czech, a Pole, a Hungarian, and two Germans. The foreigners were the good students and scholars he desired, and they also gave him non-German views. He said, "We are not the center of the world. We must concern ourselves with others and consider their interests." He frequently had lunch with individual foreign members of his staff, and he often invited them to his home and to scientific meetings. An American one day declined a request to accompany Haber to a Berlin meeting because he needed a shave. Thereupon, he was escorted to Haber's home and cordially presented with shaving necessities. Haber graciously, in courtly style, bowed himself out of the bathroom.

An associate, Frederick Kerschbaum, went to the United States in 1928 to install a phosphate processing plant in Florida. A letter from Kerschbaum told about an oven casualty and related that a replacement would be available within a week. "Ah, that is the way with you Americans," said Haber in English to a scientist dining with him (he insisted upon speaking English to all his American and British students).

"Kerschbaum passes over the disaster lightly. In American industry, if ten experiments are tried and one works, the company feels satisfied. But in Germany our funds are so limited that if we do ten experiments and one fails, everybody, from the president to the office boy, will be talking about it for the next weeks."

Of course he met foreigners on his frequent vacations outside of Germany. His favorite foreign resort was Pontresina, in Engadine near Lake Como, in Switzerland. During the war he had become better acquainted with Russia. He believed that it was primarily an agricultural country and that economic co-operation with Germany was feasible. He had seen a wooden plow on the Eastern Front in Czarist Russia. It had prompted a long discourse, when he was on furlough with friends, about culture beginning with an iron plow. He visited South America during the gold-in-seawater voyages and saw the German influence. He said, "Nothing is more delightful than to find the mother tongue and thoughts of home in remote parts of the earth." He told his audience that "German science together with German youth make the German future."

He did not visit Chile, despite an invitation, because the German ambassador to Argentina advised against the journey. Haber's nitrogen-fixation process had adversely affected the Chilean economy. He did go as far as the Christ of the Andes statue at the border. The southernmost portion of Chile had many Germans, the middle section had more Chinese, and the north had many Americans. A cousin, after being in Chile, told him that everybody in southern Chile spoke German and that Spanish could not be learned there. "My boy," said Haber, "you are saying that it is not good to go to a bar and have a drink because you can get drunk." The implication, of course, was that the country was still basically Spanish.

In 1924, Haber and his wife enjoyed a six months' round-the-world trip, and in September of that year they reached the United States. He was one of the more than seven hundred scientists present at the hundredth anniversary celebration of Philadelphia's Franklin Institute and one of the six Nobel prize winners present. He spoke to the group about "Technical Results of the Theoretical Developments of Chemistry" and gave his ideas about the relationships between pure and applied science. He said, "Nothing which man creates, either in pure or applied science, is of value for its own sake. Its advantages to mankind is the measure of its value."

He had established an Institute for Chemical Technology at the University of Berlin early in 1924 with the intention of offering students an insight into practical chemical operations. It was a paper organization, minus buildings and laboratory facilities, but under its auspices renowned industrial chemists lectured. Experts in the manufacture of soda ash or sulphuric acid or dyestuffs, were invited to speak, along with authorities in commercial research and analysis. One of Professor Schlenk's best students helped with this program. Only Haber, among all the professors, could successfully carry through the idea because he alone recognized the technical problems peculiar to Germany. He was the expert theoretician with an understanding of industry. He was called the "greatest authority in the world on the relations between scientific research and industry."

Haber said at a Franklin Institute centenary banquet, "Today your nation appears like one of the countries with an old culture. . . . The country is not dependent upon the

147

old world for either products or processes. . . . It is its own creative genius." He said that although American culture had a European base, there was no gratitude to Europe; and rightly, because similarly the hammer and the drill were used by all without thought of the toolmakers. He believed Americans to be ingenuous, industrious, and effective; thus, when preparing lead suboxide, they devised the simple procedure of exposing lead balls to the air and then bumping the spheres. He spoke as a statesman and a scientist: "This respect of mine brings to my tongue a few more words which are not addressed by a German to Americans, but by a naturalist to naturalists. . . . The banker and lawyer, the industrialist and merchant, despite their leading positions in life, are only administrative officials. The sovereign is natural science. Its progress determines the measure of prosperity of man; its cultivation is the seed from which the welfare of future generations grow."

He conjectured about a thousand-year lifespan for man at a Franklin Institute centenary press conference. He envisioned cornhusks and tree bark processed for food to provide for the increased population. "We are far enough advanced in science," he said "to know the minute difference between the structure of starch and cellulose. But we are not yet far enough advanced to be able to live on stalks of corn instead of grains of wheat." Earlier he had sent Freundlich an eight-page letter explaining the immensely important problem of aging bread. The solution was important to Germany and the conservation of grain. He had urged immediate research, and some was done.

He was the romantic type of scientist who thought about unconventional realms. His achievements and failures, conversation, stories and poetry were attuned to this attitude. His views of science was in a similar vein. "In natural science," he said, "everything is a wonder. We seemingly understand because we hear it so often. Should we forget, it is a wonder again."

He made social, political, and economic observations that ranged from commonplace to searching. Camping was then a popular recreation, and he could not understand why adults should want to play servant girl for weeks. From a more analytical standpoint, he had misgivings about America's economic balance; he sensed a coming depression. In June, 1926, he told some American physicians visiting Berlin, "You live in a land where personal freedom is the highest good. Your tradition honors the pioneer whose happy work changed a dangerous wilderness into an industrial state which serves its citizens. In our past times, not personal freedom but citizen organization was the highest political good. Our tradition does not honor the power to do but loyalty to duty. Our state does not serve its citizens, but the citizens the state. Therefore our Republic is different from yours. Governments take their life from the political spirit of the people, and political conceptions do not change like learned ideas through new deeds, but through new people."

During the two-week Pacific Ocean journey to Japan, he occupied himself with chess, conversation, and the inevitable work. Mrs. Haber served as a typist when needed; once the wife of a ship acquaintance helped. At the final shipboard evening costume ball, Haber wore a tuxedo plus a stamp on the back of his bald head; although appreciated as humor, this costume was not a prize winner.

Haber's interest in Japan had been aroused fifty years earlier by his Uncle Ludwig, the youngest of his father's brothers, who had been the first German consul to the country. At the age of thirty-two, Ludwig Haber had been murdered by Hidichika Tasaki, a fanatical samurai; these soldiers, serving war lords, opposed foreign influences. The Japanese government had offered compensation for the death, but the Haber family had refused the money because, they said, wealth could not substitute for the deceased. During Fritz Haber's visit, a memorial service for his uncle was held at Hakodate on the Yezo River, north of Tokyo. Haber had become more interested in the country through Japanese students in his laboratory; one, Setsuro Tamaru, had been at Karlsruhe and Dahlem. Just before Japan's declaration of war, Haber gave a dinner party in honor of the departing Tamaru, who went to work for the Mitsui combine.

The real reason for Haber's invitation to Japan was the country's desire for technical knowledge and help. The Japanese wanted to learn to make for themselves the enormous tonnage of dyestuffs delivered as reparations. They wanted to develop other chemical industries. Officials in Japan believed that Haber was the man to whom to convey these wishes. But German policy was to refuse assistance. The Foreign Office asked Haber not to divulge any information and to transmit all proposals to it.

Haber was the guest of the industrial pharmacist and patent medicine king, Hajime Hoshi. A former student in Germany, Hoshi had been awarded an honorary doctorate by the Charlottenburg Engineering College. Hoshi Company photographers were almost constantly with Haber. He was lionized everywhere and made to feel like a visiting potentate, overwhelmed with presents, receptions, and compliments. This seemed to be a standard treatment for important Westerners. Albert Einstein was also idolized in Japan.

Accompanied by the German ambassador and Sanskrit scholar Wilhelm Solf, Haber toured several cities. He saw well-equipped laboratories. The factories, however, did not impress him; he said Japan had a "cut-flower economy"—

without the roots of a basic heavy industry. In formal addresses, he spoke about Japanese culture and society, except for a technical talk at Kyoto Imperial University on December 2. He believed the order of occidental influence was first American, second English, and third German. "Art is really the light of Japan," he said. He was intrigued by the painting, sculpture, and floral arrangements; Mrs. Haber collected some objects of art. He saw techniques of human relations developed to a higher degree than in the West, but he criticized the excessive formality as a burden.

Drawn to Japan, he urged a closer relationship between that country and Germany. He suggested the establishment of joint institutes in Berlin and Tokyo for the exchange of scientific knowledge and the advancement of culture. The German-Japan Institute was dedicated in Berlin in June, 1926. At the inauguration Haber sent the message, "We believe that, in the long run, every nation will best serve other nations, as well as itself, by learning to understand their thoughts and feelings." His education, as well as the education of his contemporaries, was definitely not intended to mold world citizens, but now he saw the necessary first practical step taken. In June, 1927, the Japan-German Institute was formally opened in Tokyo. The German government's first gift was a seven-thousand-dollar library.

Haber had other experiences with other nations. In April, 1928, he attended in Madrid the fiftieth anniversary celebration of the Spanish Physics and Chemistry Society. In France his lecture in French about chemist Claude Louis Berthollet enraptured his audience. Through his efforts, the German Chemical Societies Union was established in 1928 with a program for international co-operation. He was on the board of directors of the International Union of Chemistry from 1929 to 1933; in 1931 he was elected vice-president; in 1932 he was solicited to be the next president, effective in 1934. Since 1913 he had been an honorary member of the American Academy of Arts and Sciences. The United States National Academy of Sciences elected him to membership in 1932. In 1931 he became an honorary member of the *Société Chimique de France* and, in 1932, of the Academy of Science of the U.S.S.R. In 1931 the Chemical Society of England and the Society of Chemical Industry in London gave him honorary memberships. One other election that pleased him was to the International Red Cross.

In 1930 the *New York Times* called him "the clue to Germany's revival." The paper's foreign correspondent was told by scientists and other distinguished Germans, "Haber is our greatest man." In 1930, Haber was named in the United States as a "remaker of civilization" along with Thomas Edison, Madame Curie, and others. In 1932 the American Academy of Arts and Sciences awarded him the biennial Rumford prize. The award is made (according to a letter from Count Rumford to the Academy, July, 1796) "to the author of the most important discovery or useful improvement . . . made . . . in any part of the Continent of America or in any of the American Islands . . . on Heat, or on Light." Previous winners of the medal include Sir Humphry Davy in 1816, Michael Faraday in 1846, and Louis Pasteur in 1856.

✠

13. Government-Science Schism

✠

ONE OF HABER'S FIRST INTRODUCTIONS to politics had come
during World War I. He had told his wife and son that
Chancellor Bethmann-Hollweg was being dismissed, and
Hermann, fifteen years old, had suggested school teacher
Georg Michaelis as the likely successor. The next morning,
Hans Gaede, in charge of civilian affairs at general head-
quarters, informed Haber of Michaelis' selection. A nationalist with a sympathy for oligarchy, Haber was always a
political observer, never a participant. In 1928, he visited
Wilhelm II in exile at Doorn, Holland, and he was repeatedly asked by the former Kaiser, "Why don't the people call
me back?" Haber later told his friends, "The man is retired.
Foolishly, he thinks he has a chance to return." Haber felt
some nostalgia for and gratitude to the old Kaiser, but when
a newspaper editor asked him for a report of his visit, he
did not co-operate. He would not serve as Wilhelm's sound-
ing board in republican Germany. When a notable visited
the institute, Haber pointed to a bricked-up section as the
place through which the Kaiser had entered; no longer a
door, it was a symbol that the Republic reigned.

He was friendly with Friedrich Ebert, the first president
of the Republic. But Haber did not really believe in the
Republic; he tolerated it. Soon after the 1929 depression,

Haber told an American scientist, "I don't know what will happen to Germany. For a while we thought the American system would work here. But we see it will not." He was not alone in being skeptical of the new form of government. Others also had the same point of view and more converts were made as riotous political disturbances and agitation increased. In 1922, Walther Rathenau, a leader once close to the Kaiser, was killed; during the same year, more than three hundred leading Republicans were assassinated. The monarchist tradition was still very much alive; streets, parks, and public places had not been renamed; a motion picture about Frederick the Great was an attraction for months.

Haber was a member of the Democratic party. He and the leader, formerly a Viennese physician, were friendly. In 1928, Haber had the opportunity of being the presidential candidate of the small German State party. Centered in Munich, its members had solicited Richard Willstätter, who suggested Haber. In 1931, Haber spent an evening with President Paul von Hindenburg and his group and was amazed at their ignorance of political events. He believed the ruling classes needed to make some effort to solve the economic and political crisis; otherwise, a revolution seemed possible. Haber, along with many others in Germany, underestimated Adolf Hitler and the Nazi party. One day in 1932 he heard Hitler speak over the radio. "Give me a gun," he told his secretary, "so I can shoot him."

In January, 1933, Adolf Hitler became chancellor of Germany. Five days after being in office, on February 4, 1933, the Nazis, with the approval of President von Hindenburg, invoked the emergency clause of the Weimar Constitution. They secured control of all public meetings and publications. One day after the Reichstag fire, February 28, the civil rights provision of the constitution was suspended;

freedom of speech, press, and assembly became a myth. Personal correspondence, telegrams, and telephone conversations were subject to scrutiny. Communist, radicals, and outspoken liberals were arrested. Eight days later, preliminary investigations were suspended; the Nazis were granted unrestricted police authority. Finally the Enabling Act of March 24 gave the regime complete dictatorial power.

Most men and women did not understand the events of the first three months of 1933. Wishful thinking was rampant. They discounted Hitler's threat to stay in office regardless of the outcome of the elections. They cited the slight Nazi loss of vote in 1932 and disregarded the steady National Socialist gain. Liberal intellectuals searched the records of history and uncovered a French general, Georges Boulanger, who had served France for a short while after the disorders of 1870. Hitler, many liberals said, was the German Boulanger. Others comforted themselves with economic trends and the inconsistent policy of National Socialism. The conservatives were badly misled. Some expected Hitler to be a figurehead chancellor. But they could not challenge the Nazi opposition to Communists in the Reichstag, and, with the Reds excluded, the Nazis had a majority ready to make a stand.

Haber spoke to Hilferding late in February. The future seemed dark and uncertain, Hilferding said, but, he claimed, Hitler would not take strong measures in view of the firm and united attitude of the trade unions. Foreign relations would suffer because Hitler had repeatedly shown contempt for the Versailles treaty. During the spring, Haber's political discussions, along with others, concerned the possibilities of the army's allowing Hitler to proceed. The brown shirts competed with the military. Too, the Allies, noting unrestricted rearmament, would be disturbed. Many

155

hoped that a change of government or an occupation of Germany would ensue.

Herbert Freundlich was one who realized the dangers of Naziism. On April 21, he requested a leave from the institute. He left Germany with all his belongings, startling English friends. They did not expect him to behave as though the Nazi revolution were irreversible.

When Nazi university students posted a manifesto which libeled Jewish professors, James Franck resigned. On April 18 he asked journalists, "How can I teach students or examine them if they think about me and my forefathers like that?"

Karl Bosch, one of the few scientists ever to defy Hitler in a personal interview, made an attempt to organize scientist resistance. In April, 1933, he came to Berlin intending to form an organization of non-Jewish German professors. He wanted Max Planck to lead, but Planck was then in Italy. Another Nobel prize winner who was approached for the job urged the selection of a younger man. The third choice was not enthusiastic, so Bosch's efforts were futile. Bosch nonetheless continued such singular and heroic efforts as maintaining Jewish scientist Hartmut Kallmann in a private I. G. Farben laboratory.

One of Haber's research students, Count H. D. von Schweinitz, attempted to marshal anti-Nazi resistance. He left Dahlem to contact his friends. But ten days after his departure he returned, announcing, "We cannot draw our swords for the Jews."

Reaction of scientists was varied. Psychologist Wolfgang Köhler came to class meetings saying, "Heil Hitler. I only say this because I am ordered by the government." Some scientists became supporters of National Socialism. Nobel prize winners Johannes Stark and Philipp Lenard were in the fold early. The only Haber student who became an ardent Nazi was a 1907 Karlsruhe student, A. Weber; son of an industrialist, he had lost a leg during the war. A renowned physicist claimed that the brown-shirt movement was "only a shower which will soon be over." A brilliant chemist believed a few Polish Jews would leave Germany and that their exodus would terminate the crisis.

Haber had a disinclination for Polish Jews. Along with a great number of other German Jews, he thought they were upstarts from the East. His prejudice was intense enough for him to have to guard against a lack of objectivity when dealing with them. This was similar to the kind of anti-Semitism he had experienced and had cited as a cause of some of his professional frustrations. He scored anti-Semitism as being unjust, but since he believed that Jews in civilized countries had a chance, the problem was minor to him. Being highly successful himself, he felt no empathy with Jews not yet in his category.

Haber continually attempted to dissociate himself from Judaism. During World War I, one of his assistants had asked him to approve the employment of several laboratory boys with decidedly Jewish names. He remarked, "We cannot have all prophets here." He advised his second wife to baptize their children, making the statement, "Do not turn the wheels back." He was sensitive about his ancestry and did not like to discuss it. At a 1920 dinner party one guest asked Karl Neuberg how it happened that he had not become a full professor until an advanced age. "Because I am a Jew," Neuberg had answered. The next morning at 8:00 A.M Haber was protesting in Neuberg's nearby house, claiming that Neuberg's statement would lead to no good. He tried to impress the Jews in his institute with the importance of abandoning their Jewish ties, and only one or two remained unbaptized. He cautioned one ardent Zionist, "It is bad enough for your career that you are Jewish. Being a Zionist also makes it worse." He thought that a home in Palestine was perfectly suitable for Polish and Russian Jews, but not German ones.

Occasionally Haber went to a Dahlem church; he told Professor Schlenk that he had become a Protestant out of conviction. Nonetheless, Haber was forever a Jew. He had married Jewish women, was surrounded by Jewish friends, and in the eyes of some persons displayed characteristics of the Eastern Jews he fervently disliked. His successful intimate friends remained Jews.

James Franck had shown courage in battle during the war and was considered for promotion. During the deliberations one superior officer mentioned Jewishness as an objection, and Franck was immediately voted down by the others. Haber's best friend, Richard Willstätter was even more involved in the Jewish question. Willstätter's teacher, Adolf von Baeyer, repeatedly came to his pupils with the request, "When are you going to be baptized?" When Willstätter succeeded this professor in 1915, the King of Bavaria said to a court attendant, "This is the last time I make a Jew a professor." In 1925 the University of Munich sought a replacement for a retiring professor of mineralogy. The incumbent favored a German Jew then at Oslo, Norway, but the Dean of Faculties had anti-Semitic feelings and the man was not appointed. Willstätter resigned in protest, but at the same time remained a good friend of the Dean.

The somewhat more than half a million Jews who lived in Germany in 1933 made up less than one per cent of the total population. More than seventy per cent of the Jews were in the larger cities. One-third of them were fifty years old or older, whereas only twenty per cent of all Germans were in the same age group. In 1933 the Aryan clause of the Civil Service Law of the Third Reich was applied, and Jews were deprived of their jobs. The Civil Service Law was ironical by reason of the number of Jewish scientists employed in government laboratories. They had remained mainly because of inability to find other suitable positions. This was true even for many of the Nobel prize winners— one-third of Germany's Nobel prize winners in science were Jewish or of Jewish ancestry.

Haber recognized the difficulty of placing the personnel of his institute elsewhere. When, in 1931, one of his associates was invited to a United States school, Haber urged acceptance of the appointment. "I am an old man," he said. "Who can tell what can happen?" The scientist left unwillingly. Another had an offer in England but refused it. Haber was displeased and threatened not to renew the man's four-year contract, usually an automatic procedure. The man preferred the pleasant association with Haber and whatever extra income consultation fees might yield. He needed the extra income. In 1928, an American National Research Council Fellow at the institute received a higher stipend than the associate directors.

In April, 1933, a National Socialist Action Committee was formed at the Kaiser Wilhelm Institute for Physical Chemistry and Electrochemistry. Organized at the request of the Nazis, this group had three charter members. A mechanic, formerly employed at Siemanns and Company, was the only willing organizer. Haber persuaded a janitor to find a third person and form the committee.

During the morning of April 21, 1933, Haber received a telephone call from the Nazi Ministry of Art, Science, and Popular Education. The ministry advised him that work at the institute could not continue with the present staff. He was urged to go to their offices and plan a reorganization. As a result Haber called an early afternoon meeting of his chief assistants. "When you go," said Freundlich, "take my resignation with you." His letter stated an inability to work with a government demanding prescribed racial antecedents for scientific work. Haber advised rewording of the letter because strong language would achieve no good end. The discussion then centered about who was Jewish. Haber went to the ministry the same afternoon, where he was told that the many Jews in his laboratory created an intolerable situation. Thereupon he insisted, "I must have my dismissal." The officials retreated. Offering apologies and insisting that he was not meant, they refused to consider the proposal. "You are a famous man," they told him. "We could not think of such a thing." They flattered him with the truth, and he consented to their demands: Freundlich and Polanyi were to leave immediately; other Jews were to be dismissed within three months. (One man, believing Haber was thus trying to discharge him appealed to another institute director for protection.)

On Monday, April 23, the acting director of the Kaiser Wilhelm institutes, Friedrich Glum, returned. He announced that the entire affair had been a mistake. He went to the ministry and returned with the Freundlich and Polanyi resignations. Only the lower assistants were meant, he said; the others were exempt. But Freundlich and Polanyi did not rescind their resignations. They told Haber and Glum that they were definitely leaving.

Haber was undecided about the new arrangement. He spoke to von Cranach, secretary of the Kaiser Welhelm institutes, who repeated the dictum of the Nazis. He wrote to President Max Planck, then in Italy, asking for friendly

advice and the date of his return. Planck replied that everything would be settled. Haber next turned to Friedrich
Schmitt-Ott, who had been active with him in the *Notgemeinschaft* and was in the ministry office. Schmitt-Ott said
he was leaving for a short rest for his health; if Haber insisted on his help, he would remain. Haber noted from the
tone of the letter that the man's health was poor, and he
did not insist.

He decided to compromise. An assistant, Dr. Georg Gerullis, received him at the ministry office. Haber was told
that the anti-Semitic policy was firmly adopted and change
was not contemplated. Moreover, the ministry did not want
anything as sensational as Haber's resignation. He was an
old official and could hold his office in accordance with the
so-called Law of Officials. Disagreement prevailed toward
the end of the discussion, and Gerullis warned, "Be careful;
we can also treat you differently." As Haber left, he was
advised to behave as did Bismarck's successor, Count Leo
von Caprivi, who, when dismissed from his post by the
Kaiser, had made no public issue of the matter.

Haber sent a resignation letter on April 30. He asked
to be released from his post on October 1. He wrote, "According to the law of April 1, 1933, I am derived from Jewish
parents and grandparents. . . . I tender my resignation with
the same pride with which I have served my country during
my lifetime. . . . For more than forty years I have selected
my collaborators on the basis of their intelligence and their
character and not on the basis of their grandmothers, and
I am not willing for the rest of my life to change this method
which I have found so good." He was summoned to the ministry and again received by an assistant. Haber said that if
the minister, Bernhard Rust, were pressed for time, he, Ha-

ber, would make another appointment. He no longer wanted to see anyone who was not in full authority. Rust did not receive him.

Several weeks later, Rust, in a public address, mentioned receipt of a letter from a German Jew, a chemist. Not mentioning Haber by name, he said the man had written that he always chose collaborators solely on the basis of their qualifications. This, said Rust, was a practice absolutely incompatible with the modern development of Germany. A few days later Haber was informed by letter that his resignation had been accepted. He became one of the thousand or more scientists and scholars forced out by the Nazis during their first year in power.

When his resignation was accepted, Haber was surprised and for a time sorely indignant. He had miscalculated its effect upon the Nazis. He had admonished an assistant to "remember the seven at Göttingen." During the 1848 revolution seven university professors at Göttingen University had threatened resignation to win a point. They were successful. The Nazis, however, did not respect learning and scholarship, and Haber's stratagem against them passed unnoticed.

Haber was disturbed about the lack of support from his friends in industry, particularly the *Interessen Gemeinschaft Farbenindustrie*, the giant chemical complex that included the *Badische Anilin und Soda Fabrik*. Max Planck, too, was a disappointment. In May, when the Kaiser Wilhelm Society held its twenty-second annual meeting, Planck said that Germans could not be permitted to stand aside "rifle at rest." He claimed "the consolidation of all available forces for the reconstruction of the fatherland" to be necessary. Later Planck showed signs of rebellion. He defended Jewish scientists in a conversation with Hitler. The government became embarrassed, and Planck was warned not to have such ideas if he valued his respect in scientific circles. Said Hitler, "Our national policies will not be revoked nor modified, even for scientists. If the dismissal of Jewish scientists means the annihilation of contemporary German science, then we shall do without science for a few years!"

Haber continued to receive his salary until October 1, and he remained in Dahlem until late summer. Then Professor Gerhard Jander of Göttingen University was appointed deputy director, and Haber sent this message to his staff: "With these words I say farewell to the Kaiser Wilhelm Institute, which was established by the Leopold Koppel Foundation at my suggestion through the work of the late architect Ihne, and which under my leadership has striven for twenty-two years to serve mankind in peace and the Fatherland in war. So far as I can judge the result, it has been favorable and has brought things of value both to science and to the defense of our land. The success is to be credited to a happy selection and to the creative power of my associates. I thank them all, and hope that the Institute under its new direction may find equally valuable men as associates and that it may maintain a name of honor and merit increasing respect in the eyes of the scientific world."

As the aged Galileo had discussed matters with church representatives during the Inquisition, so Haber had attempted to gain concessions from the Nazis. Galileo had been persecuted for supposedly subversive ideas; Haber was threatened because of ancestry and failure to submit to Nazi demands. The Grand Duke of Tuscany and his papal representative had defended Galileo; certain colleagues in science had attempted to intervene for Haber. The first scientist of the Renaissance, rapidly becoming blind, had been allowed to remain in his closely guarded home; but Haber, though ill, was not given permission to live in Dahlem. As Galileo, although conceding to the church, had ushered in a new era of science, so perhaps Haber, however much defeated by the Nazis, will have stimulated a new generation of scientists to serve mankind and to become aware of the social implications of their discoveries. Fritz Haber's experience was one of the first indications of a schism between government and science.

✠

14. In Exile

✠

THE OUTLOOK was not bright for the dismissed Jewish scientists, more German than Austrian-born Hitler or Egyptian-born Hess or Russian-born Rosenberg. Uprooted from their native land as aliens, they had to be transplanted into other lands as aliens.

Beginning in May, 1933, Haber spent a large portion of his time finding suitable positions for his staff. All his scientific workers left, except one named Horn in Polanyi's department. Haber urged his men not to compete for posts; he gave counsel about foreign countries; he wrote such advice as, "I am afraid you will find later how much one must sacrifice if separated completely from a past life." His task was difficult despite the presence of a number of American university presidents in Germany. Haber wrote a colleague, "I notice foreign countries are willing to give temporary help but not permanent positions; it would jeopardize opportunities for their own people."

He received an invitation to the Cambridge laboratory of Sir William J. Pope, who had known him since his Karlsruhe days. In Germany during the summer of 1933, Pope saw Haber's plight and offered laboratory hospitality and office facilities. Haber asked Pope whether he could also bring his sweetheart—a mythical character. His daughter,

Eva, was to live with him after her fifteenth year; or perhaps he had in mind getting his secretary or former wife out of Germany. His permitted party included only his sister, Mrs. Freyhan, and an assistant.

Late in the summer of 1933, Haber left Germany and went to Spain. He was a representative of the German Chemical Society at a meeting in Santander. During his lecture he had one of his heart spasms. Another scientist, from France, also suffered a heart attack during his own lecture and died soon afterwards. Haber next visited his son in Paris, and then he traveled to Holland and England. Returning to Paris, he prepared for a stay in Basel, Switzerland, and then for a trip to Berlin; he even sent his secretary a telegram giving his probable arrival time in Berlin.

The nearer he came to Germany, the more angina pectoris attacks plagued him. Friends laboriously tried to dissuade him from making the trip by arguing that he had no real business in the country; he should avoid trouble and excitement; he might not be allowed to leave a second time; his bitter resignation letter might be held against him. Haber claimed that a sense of duty impelled him. He wanted to return to get everything in order for his successor. He wanted the transfer to proceed quietly and orderly. He wanted permission to quit the country. He argued that he was recognized as being domiciled in Germany and was merely on a visit abroad. Without official recognition of his departure, he felt he would be regarded as a fugitive. He was fearful that he would not be allowed to return even "to visit the graves of my father and mother." The day before he planned to leave for Germany, Hermann Schmitz, an official of the *Interessen Gemeinschaft,* also in Basel, advised him not to return to his native land; Haber heeded the advice of the industrialist.

If Haber intended to fight the Nazis from within Germany, he never revealed such a plan to his friends and relatives. Yet he had a record in science of accomplishments and attempted accomplishments of the seemingly impossible. It was only after learning of the negative attitude of a possible ally, a representative of the chemical industry, that he decided not to return. No doubt, too, he was motivated by his nineteenth-century-induced desire for order and propriety.

He planned a stay at a health resort at Locarno in southern Switzerland. While waiting at Brigue to proceed to Locarno, he visited Professor Chaim Weizmann at the latter's hotel, 3,500 feet above sea level. A Russian-born British subject, Weizmann was a Zionist leader. His scientific aid to Britain during the war had been outstanding; he had found means to produce cheaply large amounts of acetone, desperately needed for explosives, by discovering bacteria which acted upon corn mash to produce the chemical. Asked what reward he wanted for the accomplishment, Weizmann had requested a British guarantee of a homeland, Palestine, for the Jewish people. Fritz Haber had met Weizmann through his son, Hermann, who was employed in a Paris chemical organization headed by Weizmann's brother-in-law, Blumenfeld.

Haber and Weizmann represented the acme of two opposing perspectives of Jews. One, Haber, became a German nationalist; the other, Weizmann, became a Jewish nationalist. The former gave up his Judaism to be a German; the latter, although he had British citizenship and gave allegiance to Britain, gave his first loyalty to Judaism.

The Zionist leader had sent a courier to Haber when the Nazi storm had struck the Dahlem institutes, offering Haber a position at the Daniel Sieff Research Institute in Palestine,

but Haber had declined the invitation, saying that acceptance would signify tacit approval of Zionism. He had fought
such "barbarian nationalism" and was not prepared to yield
his past attitudes and beliefs.

Gradually, with the pressure of events, Haber's position
modified. Once, for example, an assistant inadvertently remarked that sending an Eastern Jew from his laboratory
to a Western country would be poor policy. Haber protested,
"Since when are Jews second rate?" Late in 1933 he could
not understand why a colleague did not wish to go to Palestine. With Weizmann's help, he placed many of his students
and assistants in countries outside Germany.

At the start, while the Nazis consolidated their power and
boasted of a thousand years' rule, he told a relative, "This
will last for twelve years." In later months he had other
ideas. He said to a colleague who suggested a mild reprimand for National Socialism, "You are like a man with a
little fan standing in opposition to an enormous stream
of hot volcanic lava. Waving a bit will not stop these people." To his friend Richard Willstätter, in Germany, he
wrote, "They'll kill you and burn your house." Willstätter
did have to leave Germany.

The two scientists, Weizmann and Haber, had a very
friendly conversation. Both had strong personalities. One
suffered from the trauma of changing values and beliefs in-
duced by external events, while the other had a point of
view seemingly strengthened by the German upheaval.
Haber agreed that Weizmann had been right and he wrong.
He offered Weizmann a library of five hundred volumes
and asked a place in Palestine for his faithful secretary, Miss
Cracauer. Weizmann again invited him to the country,
promising to make him head of the physical chemistry department at the Daniel Sieff Institute; he would need to serve

only several months a year and would have an assistant to take over the remainder of the time. Haber agreed, providing he found the climate and living conditions suitable.

The next morning Haber was severely ill. A nurse had to accompany him back to his hotel. He remained in bed a few days, but recovery was slow. His son, Hermann, consequently decided against the original destination of Locarno because of its altitude. Fritz Haber stayed at a sanatorium near Lake Constance from the end of August until the beginning of October.

At that time Haber went to Cambridge University, England, in response to Sir William J. Pope's earlier invitation. He stayed at the Cambridge Arms Hotel, and the establishment was astonished when he asked for a room that would be heated mornings. The English practice was for evening warmth only. They could, however, serve his other unusual needs, a kipper for breakfast at midday and a blackboard. He held student seminars in his quarters.

The air in Cambridge was too humid for him; the foggy weather affected his health. He felt, too, that an aversion to him existed. A glassblower in the laboratory did remark, "I hear Fritz Haber is in Cambridge. That poison gas fellow ought to be shot." The laboratory belonged to Pope, active in the British Chemical Warfare Service (1914–18), developer of a new method for making mustard gas. In Germany Haber had been the one and only Haber; in England he was only a German scientist; thus some discomfort resulted from his secondary position.

In addition, National Socialism remained an irksome matter. Some of his relatives, friends, and colleagues remained in Germany, and he feared for them. One day he received a distasteful letter from a German scientist. The German government, Haber was told, knew about his disloyal expressions of opinion and demanded an explanation. He had hoped for a change of government in his country or a warning to Germany from England and France. In October, 1933, Germany left the League of Nations and the small refugee colony in England hopefully awaited a reprimand for the Hitler regime. On January 25, 1934, after dining with Herbert Freundlich at Russell's Hotel in London, Haber said, "We'll be seeing each other again behind the fences of a concentration camp." He expected England to invade Germany and intern all the German nationals, including himself and Freundlich.

He retained some semblance of the old Haber. He was gratified when English students enjoyed his wit and delivery. As a dinner guest at the home of scientist F. G. Donnan, he composed verses to a charming woman, Mrs. Katz, whose witty conversation he appreciated. He planned and was "full of future" for former associates who visited him.

On January 26, 1934, Haber went to Switzerland and the Riviera for a short vacation. His physicans had recommended an annual winter rest. Relatives had urged him to start earlier, but he had postponed the trip in order to complete a research project. His physicians consented to his journey to Palestine, but only after recuperation in Switzerland. He planned to attend the opening ceremonies for the Sieff Institute. Richard Willstätter was to be present, too.

The trip, with his sister, to Lugano, Switzerland, was scheduled for three days. He spent Sunday, January 28, with his son and the latter's brother-in-law, Dr. Rudolf Stern. As 10:00 P.M., he retired feeling well. One hour later he had a heart attack. At 3:00 A.M., Dr. Stern gave a morphine injection. Despite some gains at first, his condition became worse. At noon on Monday, January 29, Dr. Rudolf Staehelin of Basel was called. Dr. Staehelin removed four hundred centimeters of blood, and a slight improvement was noticed. After the effect of bloodletting diminished, another morphine injection was given, but to no avail. Haber died in his sleep at 5:30 P.M., January 29, 1934. Coronary sclerosis was cited as the cause of his death. Some time later his body was cremated.

✠

15. Commemorations

✠

IN 1934 some German scientists were courageous enough
to praise Haber. Alwin Mittasch wrote a worthy obituary for
the *Interessen Gemeinschaft* house organ. Max von Laue
wrote in *Die Naturwissenschaften*, "Themistocles did not go
down in history as an exile . . . but as the victor at Salamis."
He invited Haber's students to complete their research in
his laboratory. Organic chemist Schlenk had strong anti-
Nazi sentiments and was exiled to Tübingen University. A
colleague he tried to influence retorted, "Dear friend
Schlenk, you can go to a concentration camp, but not I."

Eulogies were lavish outside Germany. *Nature* magazine
published a long article by O. H. Wansbrough-Jones.
Chemistry and Industry commented: "It is sad to think
that he spent the last months of his distinguished life an
exile from his native land, finding a friendly welcome in
England, which sixteen years ago was filled with feelings
of great hostility toward Germany and Haber. We are not
fully acquainted with the cause of his exile but believe it
to be due to the descent of his ancestors from that Semitic
race from whom we Europeans learned 3,000 years ago our
alphabet and 2,000 years ago our religion." The *Chemical
Age* noted: "Of late years we have welcomed him, an anglo-
phile of most unusual breadth of and liberality of outlook,

a close observer of affairs. Under happier conditions, had he been allowed, he might well have played a leading part in smoothing out difficulties and reconciling diversities which now hold nations apart. In losing him, we lose a great man whom we can ill-spare."

A number of learned societies in Germany planned to commemorate the first anniversary of his death. These intentions became known to the Minister of Education, who sent warnings to prospective participants. Bernhard Rust wrote on January 15, 1935: "The Kaiser Wilhelm Society, in cooperation with the German Chemical Society, as well as the German Physical Society, has sent out invitations to a Memorial Ceremony for Fritz Haber on Tuesday, January 29, at Harnack House in Berlin-Dahlem.

"Professor Dr. Haber was dismissed from his office on October 1, 1933, on the basis of a proposal in which his inner attitude against the present state was unambiguously expressed, and which public opinion was forced to interpret as a criticism of the measures adopted by the National Socialist state. The intention of the above-named society to sponsor a Memorial Service on the occasion of the first anniversary of Haber's death must in the light of this fact be interpreted as a challenge to the National Socialist state. All the more so since special commemorations of the first anniversary of a death are given only in especially exceptional cases to the *greatest* Germans.

"This interpretation is confirmed by the fact that the sponsors have not shrunk from urging those invited to the ceremony to appear in uniform.

"I must therefore forbid all my subordinates sworn in as state officials to participate in the ceremony."

Notwithstanding the ultimatum, on January 29, 1935, more than five hundred scientists, soldiers, industrialists, and teachers gathered in Dahlem to pay tribute to Haber. His military friends attended the two-hour ceremony, but many of his professional colleagues were absent. Max Planck opened the services with the Nazi salute. He said: "Then came the moment when under the Civil Service Law in the Third Reich, Haber had to part company with his trusted associates to whom he felt himself bound. He was no longer able to endure his position and offered his resignation and went abroad. He will retain in the annals of science, as in the history of the Kaiser Wilhelm Institute, a place of honor. Therefore we reward loyalty with loyalty and pay our earnest tribute at this moment to the German scholar and German soldier, Fritz Haber." The Klinger quartet played after the four speakers. The first was scheduled to be K. F. Bonhoeffer, but Otto Hahn read his speech. Rust had given clearance to Bonhoeffer, but a Nazi subordinate prevented his entrance when he arrived at Harnack House. Bonhoeffer's brother, Dietrich, the eminent theologian, was executed by the Nazis in April, 1945; his sister had been murdered by the Nazis in 1934.

A service was held in Palestine coincident with the opening of the Haber Library in the Daniel Sieff Institute. (Many of the books in the library bear Haber's signature.) Haber's former students, Bergmann and Farkas, as well as Chaim Weizmann, spoke in Hebrew. Weizmann kept photographs of two scientists on his desk at his Rehovoth Institute—Willstätter and Haber.

Haber's name and influence was slowly removed within Germany. An *Ortsgruppe* Dahlem of the National Socialist German Workers party, the Nazis, reigned at the scientific center of Dahlem; Hitler was in Harnack House three times between June, 1934, and June, 1935. The Nazis set thick-foliaged plants around the Haber stone and oak tree, completely hiding the memorial. When an English student asked permission to visit the laboratory, he was told curtly, "No." The Nazis complained when Max Planck praised Haber at the twenty-fifth anniversary of the Kaiser Wilhelm Society in January, 1936. Haber is mentioned twice in the published account of the proceedings; the new disorder scarcely recognized his contributions.

In November, 1939, with Germany and England opponents in World War II, the *Journal of the Chemical Society* published a thirty-page appreciation of Haber and his work by J. E. Coates.

At ceremonies commemorating the twelfth anniversary of his death, held on February 2, 1946, the memorial tree in Dahlem was rededicated. Many dignitaries were present, and one address was given by a former assistant, Hartmut Kallmann. The Nazis could no longer interfere.

The fortieth anniversary of the founding of the Kaiser Wilhelm Institute for Physical Chemistry and Electrochemistry was observed on what would have been Fritz Haber's eighty-fourth birthday, December 9, 1952. A memorial plaque was dedicated and placed in the stairwell of the main building. Funds for the memorial were provided by the *Badische Anilin und Soda Fabrik*, the *Metallgesellschaft* in Frankfurt, the *Deutsche Bunsengesellschaft*, and the *Gesellschaft Deutscher Chemiker*. The inscription on the memorial tablet reads:

THEMISTOCLES

entered history not as the exile at the court of the Persian King, but as the victor of Salamis.

HABER

will live in history as the brilliant discoverer

of that method of combining nitrogen with hydrogen which is the basis of the technical fixation of atmospheric nitrogen, as the man who created, as was stated at his receipt of the Nobel Prize, "an exceedingly important means of advancing agriculture and the welfare of mankind," who obtained bread from air and won a triumph "in the service of his country and all mankind."

✠

The Publications and Lectures of Fritz Haber

✠

(In Chronological Order)

(With C. Liebermann). "Bidioxy Methylene Indigo," *Berichte,* 23:1566–67. 1890.

"Piperonal Derivatives," *Berichte,* 24:617–26. 1891.

(With L. Knorr). "Constitution of Ethyl Diacetosuccinate," *Berichte,* 27:1151–67. 1894.

(With A. Weber). "The Combustion Products of Gas Flames," *Jour. Gasbel.,* 38:449–55. 1895.

Experimental Studies on the Decomposition and Combustion of Hydrocarbons. Munich, R. Oldenbourg, 1896.

(With H. Samoylowicz), "Hexane from Crude Gasoline," *Jour. Gasbel,* 39:435. 1896.

"Note on Oxidation Through Hydroxylamine," *Berichte,* 29:2444–45. 1896.

(With H. Oechelhäuser). "Decomposition of Hexane and Trimethylene by Heat," *Jour. Gasbel.,* 39:799–805. 1896. 39:813–18, 830–34. 1897.

"Theory of the Pyrogenic Reactions of Aliphatic Hydrocarbons," *Berichte,* 29:2691–2700. 1896.

(With H. Oechelhäuser). "Estimation of Ethylene in the Presence of Benzene Vapor," *Berichte,* 29:2700–2705. 1896.

(With A. Weber). "Combustion of Illuminating Gas on Cooled Surfaces," *Berichte,* 29:3000–3006. 1896.

(With A. Weber). "Combustion of Coal Gas in Gas Engines," *Berichte,* 30:145–51. 1897.

(With S. Grinberg). "Analysis of Coals," *Zeit. Anal. Chem.*, 36: 557–67. 1897.

"Electro-deposited Iron," *Zeit. Elek.*, 4:410–13. 1897.

"On What Important Chemical Control Apparatus in Gas Works Are Not Chemically Feasible," *Jour. Gasbel.*, 40:719. 1897.

"The Determination of the Useful Effect and Heat Loss," *Jour. Gasbel.*, 40:751. 1897.

"Gradual Electrolytic Reduction of Nitrobenzene with Limited Cathode Potential," *Zeit. Elek.*, 4:506–13. 1898.

"Electrolytic Preparation of Beta-Phenyl Hydroxylamine," *Zeit. Elek.*, 5:77–78. 1898.

(With S. Grinberg). "Electrolysis of Hydrochloric Acid," *Zeit. Anorg. Chem.* 16:198–228, 329–61. 1898.

"Electrolysis of Hydrochloric Acid and Cathodic Formation of Lead," *Zeit. Anorg. Chem.*, 16:438–49. 1898.

(With S. Grinberg). "Electrolytic Formation of Hydrogen Peroxide," *Zeit. Anorg. Chem.*, 18:37–47. 1898.

Outline of Technical Electrochemistry on a Theoretical Basis. Munich, R. Oldenbourg, 1898.

(With G. Bredig). "Pulverisation of Metal Cathodes During Electrolysis with a Constant Current," *Berichte*, 31:2741–52. 1899.

"Process for the Staining of Cotton and Other Plant Fibers with Chromium," DRP 101,481, June 3. 1898. Patentbl., 20:185. 1899.

"The Electrical Reduction of Non-electrolytes," *Zeit. Physik. Chem.*, 32:193–273. 1900.

"Electrolytic Reduction of Nitro Compounds," *Zeit. Angew. Chem.*, 13:433–39. 1900.

(With C. Schmidt). "Electrolytic Reduction of Nitrobenzene," *Zeit. Physik. Chem.*, 32:271–81. 1900.

(With St. Leskiewicz). "Determination of Benzene and Ethylene in Illuminating Gas," *Jour. Gasbel.*, 43:347–50. 1900.

"Letter to the Editor," *Jour. Gasbel.*, 43:511. 1900.

"Auto-Oxidation," *Zeit. Physik. Chem.*, 34:513–21. 1900.

(With F. Bran). "Auto-Oxidation," *Zeit. Physik. Chem.*, 35:81–93. 1900.

"Production of New Resistance by W. C. Heräus," *Zeit. Elek.*, 7:269–70. 1900.

"Electrochemistry Instruction at the Chemical-Technical Institute of the Karlsruhe Engineering College," *Zeit. Anorg. Chem.*, No. 31. 1900.

"Note on Auto-Oxidation," *Zeit. Physik. Chem.*, 35:608–609. 1901.

"Auto-Oxidation and Its Connections with the Theories of Ions and of the Galvanic Cell," *Zeit. Elek.*, 7:441–48. *Berichte*, 7:466. 1901.

"Graphic Thermodynamic Electrochemical Processes," *Phys. Zeit.*, 1:361–71. 1901.

"Ferrite Solutions," *Zeit. Elek.*, 7:215–21, 724–26. 1901.

"Reply to A. Binz on Electrochemical Reduction," *Jour. Prak. Chem.*, 64:289–93. 1901.

(With W. Pick). "Soluble Alkali Salts of Ferric Oxide and Ferric Acid," *Zeit. Elek.*, 7:215–21. 1901.

"Electrode Potentials," *Zeit. Elek.*, 7:1043–53. 1902.

(With R. Geipert). "Aluminum Preparation," *Zeit Elek.*, 8:1–8, 26–33. 1902.

(With M. Sack). "Disintegration and Pulverisation of Cathodes Due to the Formation of Alloys with Alkali Metals," *Zeit. Elek.*, 8:245–55. 1902.

"The Potential of Alloys and the Formation of Superficial Layers," *Zeit. Elek.*, 8:541–52. 1902.

"Amalgam Potentials and the Question of Whether Metals Dissolved in Mercury are Monoatomic," *Zeit. Physik. Chem.*, 41:399–406. 1902.

"A New Cloth Print Process," *Zeit. Farben Textil. Chem.*, 1:1–12. *Zeit Angew. Chem.*, 15:1177–83. 1902.

"Aluminum Preparation," *Zeit. Elek.*, 8:607–16. 1902.

(With G. Bredig). "F. Reidel's Objection to the Reaction Mechanism," *Zeit. Angew. Chem.*, 16:557–58. 1903.

"Theory of Indigo Reaction," *Zeit. Elek.*, 9:607–608. 1903.

"Instruction and Electrochemical Techniques in the United States," *Zeit. Elek.*, 9:291–303, 347–70, 379–406, 514 ff. 1903.

"Technical Pictures from the United States and Germany's Display at the World's Fair in St. Louis," *Zeit. Elek.*, 9:893–98. 1903.

"Letter to the Editor," *Electrochemical Industry*, 1:471. 1903.

(With F. Richardt). "Equilibrium of Gases in the Bunsen Flame and Chemical Determination of Temperatures of Flames," *Zeit. Anorg. Chem.*, 38:5–64. *Jour. Gasbel.*, 47:809. 1904.

(With G. van Oordt). "Beryllium Compounds," *Zeit. Anorg. Chem.*, 38:365–68, 377–98. 1904.

(With H. Schwenke). "Electrochemical Determination," *Zeit. Elek.*, 10:143–56. 1904.

"Theory of Reaction Velocity in Heterogeneous Systems," *Zeit. Elek.*, 10:156–57. 1904.

"Order of Magnitude of the Time of Formation of Complex Molecules, Equilibrium Constants and Atomic Dimensions," *Zeit. Elek.*, 10:433–37. 1904.

(With L. Bruner). "The Carbon Cell," *Zeit. Elek.*, 10:697–713. 1904.

"Small Ionic Concentrations," *Zeit. Elek.*, 10:773–76. 1904.

(With R. Russ). "Electrical Reduction," *Zeit Physik. Elek.*, 47: 257–335. 1904.

(With G. Bredig). "Principle of Gas Separation Through Centrifugal Force," *Zeit. Angew. Chem.*, 17:452–64. 1904.

(With S. Tolloczko). "Reduction to Carbon of Chemically Combined Carbonic Acid," "Electrochemical Charges with Solid Substances," *Zeit. Anorg. Chem.*, 41:407–41. 1904.

"Preparation and Compression of Pure Gases for Research Purposes," *Jour. Gasbel.*, 47:484–85. 1904.

"Principle of Gas Separation Through Centrifugal Force," *Jour. Gasbel.*, 47:943–44. 1904.

"Fluid Separation Through Centrifugal Force," *Jour. Gasbel.*, 47:943–44. 1904.

"The Light of the Auerstrampfe," *Jour. Gasbel.*, 47:1143–44. 1904.

(Translated into German by F. Haber and M. Stocker). *Laboratory Exercises in General Chemistry by Alexander Smith.* Karlsruhe, Braunsche Publishers, 1904.

(With G. van Oordt). "Preparation of Ammonia from the Elements," *Zeit. Anorg. Chem.*, 43:111–15, 44:341–78. 47:42–44. 1905.

(With A. Moser). "Generator Gas and Carbon Cells," *Zeit. Elek.*, 11:593–609. 1905.

"The Role of Electrochemistry in Modern Technology," *Zeit. Elek.*, 11:264–71. 1905.

"Fundamental Formulae of Chemical and Electrical Energy," *Electrochem. Met. Industry*, 3:99ff. 1905.

(Translation by A. B. Lamb). *Thermodynamics of Technical Gas Reactions. Seven Lectures.* Munich, R. Oldenbourg, 1905.

"Detection and Precipitation of the Ferrous Iron in Aqueous Solutions of Potassium Ferrocyanide," *Zeit. Elek.*, 11:846–49. 1905.

(With F. Goldschmidt). "The Anodic Attack of Iron by Stray Currents in the Earth and the Passivity of Iron," *Zeit. Elek.*, 12:49–74. *Jour. Gasbel.*, 49:637,646. 1906.

(With L. Bruner). "The Carbon Cell," *Zeit. Elek.*, 12:78–79. 1906.

"Optical Analysis of Industrial Gases," *Zeit. Agnew. Chem.*, 19:1418–22. 1906.

(With F. Fleischmann). "Reversible Action of Oxygen on Magnesium Chloride," *Zeit. Anorg. Chem.*, 51:336–47. 52:127–28. 1906–1907.

(With K. Liese). "Measurement of Stray Currents in the Earth," *Zeit. Elek.* 12:829–52. 1907.

(With R. LeRossignol). "The Ammonia Equilibrium," *Berichte*, 40:2144–54. 1907.

(With W. Maitland). "The Potentials of Iron and the Passivity of the Metal," *Zeit. Elek.*, 13:309–10. 1907.

"The Gas Refractometer," *Zeit. Elek.*, 13:450–63. 1907.

(With L. LeRossignol). "Equilibrium of Ammonia Under Pressure," *Zeit. Elek.*, 14:181–96. 1907.

(With R. LeRossignol). "Position of the Ammonia Equilibrium," *Zeit. Elek.*, 14:513–14. 1907.

(With F. Fleischmann). "The Oxy-Hydrogen Cell," *Zeit. Anorg. Chem.*, 51:245–88. 1907.

(With G. W. A. Foster). "The Oxy-Hydrogen Cell," *Zeit. Anorg. Chem.*, 51:289–314. 1907.

(With W. H. Patterson). "The Oxy-Hydrogen Cell," *Zeit. Anorg. Chem.*, 51:356–68. 1907.

(With A. Koenig). "Producing Nitrogen Oxides by the Action of the Electric Arc on Air or Like Mixtures of Nitrogen and Oxygen," DRP 210,166, July 25. 1907.

(With A. Koenig). "Oxidation of Nitrogen in the High Potential Arc," *Zeit. Elek.*, 13:725–43. 14:689–95. 1908.

(With A. Rieff and P. Vogt). "Confirmation of Faraday's Law When Current Passes Through Hot Porcelain," *Zeit. Anorg. Chem.*, 51:154–73, 289, 356. 1908.

(With R. Beutner and E. Heller). "Solid Electrolytes, Their Decomposition by the Electric Current, and Their Electromotive Behavior in Galvanic Cells," *Ann. Physik.*, 26:927–73. 1908.

(With Richard and Allner). "The Bunsen Flame," *Zeit. Anorg. Chem.*, 38:5. *Jour. Gasbel.*, 48:1035ff. *Zeit. Elek.*, 14:571–74. 1908.

"The Gas Rrefractometer," *Jour. Gasbel.*, 50:1068. 1908.

(With A. Koenig). "Production of Compounds of Nitrogen and Oxygen from Atmospheric Air or Other Mixtures of Nitrogen and Oxygen," British Patent 15,490, July 21. 1908.

(With A. Koenig). "Production of Nitrogen Oxides," DRP 235,-421. 1908. DRP 223, 408. 1909.

"A Study of Hydroxylamine," *Jour. Prak. Chem.*, 79:173:76. 1909.

(With R. LeRossignol). Dissociation of Carbonic Acid in the Oxygen-Carbon Monoxide Flame," *Zeit. Physik. Chem.*, 66:181–96. 1909.

(With H. J. Hodsman). "The Composition of the Gases in Very Hot Flames," *Zeit. Physik. Chem.*, 67:343–83. 1909.

(With Z. Klemensiewicz). "Electrical Forces at Phase Boundaries," *Zeit. Physik Chem.*, 67:385–431. 1909.

(With P. Krassa). "Corrosion of Iron by Vagabond Currents from Street Railway," *Zeit. Elek.*, 15:705–12. 1909.

(With G. Just). "The Escape of Negative Electrons from Reacting Metals," *Ann. Physik.*, 30:411–15. 1909.

(With A. Koenig). "Oxidation of Atmospheric Nitrogen," *Zeit. Elek.*, 16:11–25. 1910.

(With B. S. Lacy). "The Inner Zone of the Bunsen Flame," *Zeit. Physik. Chem.*, 68:726–52. 1910.

(With J. E. Coates). "Formation of Nitrogen Oxide in the Combustion of Carbon Monoxide," *Zeit Physik. Chem.*, 69: 337–88. 1910.

"The Preparation of Ammonia from Nitrogen and Hydrogen," *Zeit. Elek.*, 16:244–46. *Chem. Ztg.*, 34:245–46. *Jour. Gasbel.*, 53:367–68. 1910.

(With G. Just). "The Production of Negative Electricity During the Reaction of Gases Upon Base Metals," *Zeit. Elek.*, 16: 275–79. 1910.

"Formation of Nitric Acid from the Air," *Zeit. Agnew. Chem.*, 23:684–89. *Chem. Ztg.*, 34:283. 1910.

(With F. Lowe). "An Interferometer for Chemists According to Rayleigh's Principle," *Zeit. Agnew. Chem.*, 23:1393–98. 1910.

(With A. Koenig and E. Platou). "The Formation of Nitrogen Oxide in the High Tension Arc," *Zeit. Elek.*, 16:796–803. 1910.

(With W. Holwech). "Formation of Nitrogen Oxide from the

Air Under Pressure in the Electric Arc," *Zeit. Elek.*, 16:810–13. 1910.

(By A. Moser, with F. Haber). *Electrolytic Processes of Organic Chemistry*. Halle, W. Knapp, 1910.

"Processes for the Preparation of Ammonia Through the Catalytic Union of Nitrogen and Hydrogen Under Pressure," DRP, 229,126, November 29. 1910.

(With A. Koenig). "Production of Oxides of Nitrogen," U. S. Patent 938,312, October 26. 1910.

(With R. LeRossignol). "Processes for the Preparation of Ammonia," U. S. Patent 971,501. 1910.

"Manufacture of Ammonia," British Patent 14,023, June 9. 1910.

(With G. Just). "The Emission of Electrons During Chemical Reactions," *Ann. Physik.*, 36:308–40. *Chem Ztg.*, 35:1073–76. *Naturw. Rundschau.*, 26:545–48, 557–60. 1911.

"An Interferometer According to Rayleigh's Principle," DRP 230,748, April 2. DRP 239,120, October 10. DRP 239,121, September 10. 1911.

"Process for the Production of Ammonia from the Elements," DRP 238,450, September 28. 1911.

"Union of Elementary Nitrogen with Oxygen and Hydrogen," *Chem. Ztg.*, 37:712. 1911. *Jour. Gasbel.* 56:514–16. 1913.

(With G. Just). "Reaction Activity," *Zeit. Elek.*, 17:592. 1911.

(With R. LeRossignol). "Production of Ammonia," Canadian Patent 133,527, June 6. U. S. Patent 1,006,206, October 17. 1911.

(With J. Zawadzki and R. LeRossignol). "The Polarization of Solid Electrolytes," *Zeit. Physik. Chem.*, 78:228–43. 1912.

"Preface to F. Hiller's Paper," *Zeit Physik. Chem.*, 81:591. 1913.

(With R. LeRossignol). "The Technical Preparation of Ammonia from Its Elements," *Zeit. Elek.*, 19:53–72. 1913.

"The Fire-Damp Whistle," *Chem. Ztg.*, 37:1329–30. *Naturw.*, 1:1049–51. 1913. *Jour. Soc. Chem. Ind.*, 33:54. *Engineer. Mag.*, 46:601 ff. 1914.

"The Production of Ammonia Through the Catalytic Combination of Nitrogen and Hydrogen," DRP 259,996, August 5. DRP 260,756, June 6. 1913.

(With F. Kerschbaum). "The Measurement of Low Pressures with a Vibrating Quartz Fiber," *Zeit. Elek.*, 20:296–305. 1914.

(With G. Just). "New Researches on Electron Emission Accompanying Chemical Reactions," *Zeit. Elek.*, 20:483–85. 1914.

(With A. Klemenc). "Electrochemical Reactions Taking Place on the Passage of Current Through the Gas-Liquid Boundary of Solutions of Electrolytes," *Zeit. Elek.*, 20:485–88. 1914.

"Modern Chemical Industry: The Hurter Memorial Lecture," *Jour. Soc. Chem. Ind.*, 33:49–54. *Jour. Ind. Eng. Chem.*, 6:325–31. 1914.

"The Synthetic Preparation of Ammonia," *Zeit. Agnew. Chem.*, 27:473–77. *Oesterr. Chem. Ztg.*, 17:165–66. *Jour. Gasbel.*, 57:789–99. 1914.

(With R. Leiser). "The Fire-Damp Whistle," British Patent 9344, April 15. 11,236, May 6. DRP 275,906, June 29. 1914.

(With R. Marc). "Kinetics of Adsorption," *Zeit. Elek.*, 20:515–24. 1914.

(With K. Bosch and A. Mittasch). "Production of Synthetic Ammonia," U. S. Patent 1,149,510, August. 1915.

"Experiments on Ammonia; General Considerations," *Zeit Elek.*, 20:597–604. 1915.

(With S. Tamaru and Ch. Ponnaz). "Determination of the Ammonia Equilibrium at Thirty Atmospheres Pressure," *Zeit. Elek.*, 21:89–106. 1916.

(With A. Maschke). "The Ammonia Equilibrium at Ordinary Pressures," *Zeit. Elek.*, 21:128–30. 1916.

(With S. Tamaru). "Determination of the Heat of Formation of Ammonia at High Temperatures," *Zeit. Elek.*, 21:191–206. 1916.

(With S. Tamaru and L. W. Oeholm). "Heat of Formation of

Ammonia at Ordinary Temperatures," *Zeit. Elek.*, 21:206–28. 1916.

(With S. Tamaru). "Specific Heat of Ammonia," *Zeit. Elek.*, 21:228–41. 1916.

(With F. C. Greenwood). "The Action of Uranium as a Catalyzer in the Synthesis of Ammonia," *Zeit. Elek.*, 21:241–45. 1916.

(With R. LeRossignol). "Synthesis of Ammonia." U. S. Patent 1,202,995, October 31. 1917.

(With R. Leiser). "The Fire-Damp Whistle," Swiss Patent 75,735, July 16. 1917.

"Properties of the Metals," *Sitz. Preuss. Adak. Wiss.*, 506–518, 990–1007. 1919.

"Considerations on the Theory of Energy Change," *Ber. Deut. Phys. Gesell.*, 21:750–68. 1920.

"Motor Combustion of Acetylene," *Zeit Elek.*, 26:325–29. 1920.

(By E. Ramm, N. Caro., F. Haber, and E. Cohn). *Nitrogen Fertilizers, Bread and Food from Coal and Air.* Pages 21–25. Berlin, R. Oldenbourg, 1920.

"Science and Industry," *Chem. Ztg.*, 44:913. 1921.

"The Emergency Society for German Science," *Chem. Ztg.*, January 8, 1921. Also in *Aus Leben und Beruf*, see under 1927.

"Amorphous Precipitates and Crystallized Sols," *Berichte*, 55:1717–33. 1922.

"Letters to the Editors," *Nature*, 109:40. 1922.

"The Age of Chemistry, Its Problems and Its Services," *Zeit. Angew. Chem.*, 35:37–40. 1922. Also in *Fünf Vorträge*, see under 1924.

"The Eightieth Birthday of Karl Engler," *Chem. Ztg.*, 46:2ff. 1922. Also in *Aus Leben und Beruf*, see under 1927.

"The Preparation of Ammonia from Nitrogen and Hydrogen," (Nobel lecture), *Nature*, 10:1041–49. 1922. Also in *Fünf Vorträge*, see under 1924.

"Bemerkung," *Naturw.*, 11:339–40. 1923.

(With W. Zisch). "Excitation of Gas Spectra by Chemical Reactions," *Zeit. Physik.*, 9:302–26. 1923.

"To the Memory of Hans Goldschmidt," *Berichte*, 55:77–79. 1923.

"The History of Gas Warfare," lecture given October 1, 1923. Also in *Fünf Vorträge*, see under 1924.

"Science and Industry after the War," lecture given March 20, 1923. Also in *Fünf Vorträge*, see under 1924.

"German Chemistry in the Last Ten Years," *Die Deut. Rundschau.*, 199:14–22. 1924. Also in *Aus Leben und Beruf*, see under 1927.

(With H. Wolff). "Mist Explosions," *Zeit. Angew. Chem.*, 36: 373–77. 1924.

"The Dissociation of the Mercury Atom," *Naturw.*, 12:635. 1924.

Fünf Vorträge aus den Jahren 1920–23 (Five lectures from the years 1920–23). Berlin, Julius Springer, 1924.

"*Speech* given at the Fiftieth Anniversary of the Academic Literary Society of the University of Breslau," June 10, 1924. Also in *Aus Leben und Beruf*, see under 1927.

"Science and Living," lecture given in Tokyo, November 17, 1924. Also in *Aus Leben und Beruf*, see under 1927.

"Japanese Impressions," lecture given in Osaka, December 4, 1924. Also in *Aus Leben und Beruf*, see under 1927.

Lecture given in Tokyo at the Ministry of Education, December, 1924. Also in *Aus Leben und Beruf*, see under 1927.

(With J. Jaenicke). "The Gold Content of Rhine Water," *Zeit. Anorg. Allgem. Chem.*, 147:156–70. 1925.

"Economic Interdependence of Germany and Japan," lecture given in Frankfurt am Main, June 11, 1925. Also in *Aus Leben und Beruf*, see under 1927.

"The Cultivation of Science," *Naturw.*, June 26, 1925. Also in *Aus Leben und Beruf*, see under 1927.

"Practical Results of the Theoretical Development of Chemistry," *Jour. Frank Inst.*, 199:437–56. 1925.

"Hydroxides of Aluminum and Tervalent Iron," *Naturw.*, 13: 1007–12. 1926.

(With J. Jaenicke and F. Matthias), "Alleged Preparation of 'Artificial' Gold from Mercury," *Zeit. Anorg. Allgem. Chem.,* 153:153–83. *Berichte,* 59:1641–48. 1926.

"Transmutation Experiments," *Metallbörse,* 16:540–41. 1926.

(With J. Jaenicke and F. Matthias). "Transmutation of Chemical Elements," *Naturw.,* 14:405–13. *Pharm. Ztg.,* 71:377–78. 1926.

"The Borderlands of Chemistry," *Naturw.,* 14.841–55. 1926. Also in *Aus Leben und Beruf,* see under 1927.

Lecture given at the opening of the German-Japan Institute, December 4, 1926. Also in *Aus Leben und Beruf,* see under 1927.

"Disarmament and Gas Warfare," lecture before the German Division of the Interparliamentary Union. *Vorwärts,* July 7, 1926.

"Corrosion as an Electrochemical Problem," *Zeit. Elek.,* 33:83. 1927.

"Science and the State," lecture given January 20, 1927. Also in *Aus Leben und Beruf* (Published 1927).

(With J. Jaenicke). "Gold in Sea Water," *Zeit. Angew. Chem.,* 40:303–14. 1927.

Aus Leben und Beruf: Aufsätze, Reden, Vorträge (Out of Life and Calling. Essays, Speeches, Lectures). Berlin, Julius Springer, 1927.

(With K. Bonhoeffer). "Band Spectroscopy and Flame Reactions," *Sitz. Preuss. Akad. Wiss.,* August 3, *Zeit. Physik. Chem.,* 137:263–88. 1928.

"The Sixtieth Birthday of Georg Bredig," *Zeit. Elek.,* 34:677–79. 1928.

"Towards an Appreciation of Justus von Liebig," *Zeit Agnew. Chem.,* 41:891–97. 1928.

(With H. D. von Schweinitz). "Ignition of Detonating Gas by Hydrogen Atoms." *Sitz. Preuss. Akad. Wiss.,* 499–506. 1928.

"Letters to the Editor," *Zeit. Elek.,* 34:711. 1928.

"Combustion Mechanism in the Bunsen Flame," *Metallbörse,* 18:960–61. 1928.

"The Role of Electricity Carrier During the Explosion of Combustible Gases Mixed with Air," *Sitz. Preuss. Akad. Wiss.*, 162–70. 1929.

"Heterogeneous Catalysis," *Zeit. Elek.*, 35:533–35. 1929.

(With L. Farkas and P. Goldfinger). "The Ignition of Detonating Gas," *Naturw.*, 17:674. 1929.

"To the Memory of Franz Oppenheim," *Zeit. Angew. Chem.*, 43:141–45. 1930.

(With J. P. Ethier). "Hydrogen Atoms as Means of Oxidizing and Reducing," *Naturw.*, 18:266. 1930.

(With L. Farkas and P. Goldfinger). "Ignition of Carbon Monoxide Detonating Mixture by Decomposition Products of Water," *Naturw.*, 18:266. 1930.

(With H. N. Alyea). "Ignition of Detonating Gas at Low Pressure by Warm Quartz," *Naturw.*, 18:441–43. 1930.

(With L. Farkas and P. Harteck). "Photochemical Sensitization of the Combustion of Hydrogen and Carbon Monoxide," *Naturw.*, 18:266–68. 1930.

"The Ignition of Detonating Gas," *Naturw.*, 18:917. 1930.

(With H. N. Alyea). "The Ignition of Mixtures of Hydrogen and Oxygen by Quartz or Porcelain at Low Pressures," *Zeit. Physik. Chem.*, 10B:193–204. 1930.

(With L. Farkas and P. Harteck). "Photochemical Sensitization in the Ultra Violet," *Zeit. Elek.*, 36:711–14. 1930.

"Bosch and Bergius," *Berliner Tageblatt*, Sunday, November 15, 1931.

(With J. Franck). "The Theory of Catalysis of Heavy Metal Ions in Aqueous Solution with Special Reference to the Auto-Oxidation of Sulfite Solutions," *Sitz. Preuss. Akad. Wiss.*, 250–56. 1931.

(With H. Sachsse). "The Reaction of Sodium Vapor with Elementary Oxygen," *Zeit. Physik Chem.*, Bodenstein Memorial Volume: 831–48. 1931.

(With R. Willstätter). "Unpairedness and Radical Chains in the Reaction Mechanism of Organic Enzymic Process," *Be-*

richte, 64B:2844-56. 1931. *Anales Soc. Espan. Fis. Quim.*, 30:244-53. 1932.

"Richard Willstätter's Sixtieth Birthday," *Naturw.*, 20:601-602. 1932.

(With F. Oppenheimer). "Inflammation of Mixtures of Hydrogen and Oxygen by Hydrogen Atoms," *Zeit. Physik. Chem.* 16Bm:443-59. 1932.

(With O. H. Wansbrough-Jones). "Auto-Oxidation Study," *Zeit. Physik. Chem.*, 18B:103-23. 1932.

(With J. Weiss). "The Catalysis of Hydrogen Peroxide," *Naturw.*, 20:948-50. 1932.

"To the 75th Birthday of the President of the Kaiser Wilhelm Society. Max Planck," *Naturw.*, 21:293. 1933.

(With J. Weiss). "The Catalytic Decomposition of Hydrogen Peroxide in Iron Salts," *Proc. Roy. Soc.* (London), 147A: 332-51. 1934.

"Chemistry in War," *Jour. Chem. Educ.*, 22:526ff. 1945. Also in *Fünf Vorträge*, see under 1924.

✠

Bibliography

✠

INTERVIEWS

Dr. Harold A. Abramson, New York, New York; Dr. Hans W. Albu, Providence, Rhode Island; Professor Hubert N. Alyea, Princeton University; Dr. Ernst B. Auerbach, Chicago, Illinois; Ernst Baerwald, Berkeley, California; Professor Wilder D. Bancroft, Cornell University; Dr. Ernst Bergmann, New York, New York; Dr. S. Berliner, Chicago, Illinois; Mrs. S. Berliner, Chicago, Illinois; Professor R. Beutner, Hahnemann Medical College; Professor K. D. Bonhoeffer, University of Chicago; Dr. Max Bredig, New York, New York; Dr. Margaret Willstätter Bruch, Winnebago, Illinois; Dr. Fred Carter, Newark, New Jersey; Dr. Hans E. Eisner, Queens, New York; Professor Kasimir Fajans, University of Michigan; Dr. A. Farkas, Philadelphia, Pennsylvania; Dr. L. Farkas, Hebrew University; Herbert Fleischmann, Fort Thomas, Kentucky; Dr. P. Flint, Nutley, New Jersey; Dr. G. R. Fonda, Schenectady, New York; Professor James Franck, University of Chicago; Mrs. Elizabeth Freund, Philadelphia, Pennsylvania; Professor Herbert Freundlich, University of Minnesota; Professor Richard Goldschmidt, University of California (Berkeley); Miss Claire Haber, University of Chicago; Dr. Hermann Haber, Great Neck, New York; Rudolf Haber, New York, New York; Dr. Ernst Hauser, Massachusetts Institute of Technology; Dr. Wilhelm Hirschkind, Pittsburg, California; Dean Matthew A. Hunter, Troy, New York; Professor V. N. Ipatieff, Chicago, Illinois; Dr.

191

Frederick Kerschbaum, Dayton, Ohio; Professor V. I. Komarewsky, Illinois Institute of Technology; Dr. Charles T. Krieger, New York, New York; Professor Rudolf Ladenburg, Princeton University; Professor Arthur Lamb, Harvard University; Dr. Irving Langmuir, Schenectady, New York; Mrs. Agnes Haber Little, Chicago, Illinois; Professor Hermann Mark, Brooklyn Polytechnical Institute; Erich Marx, Los Angeles, California; Mrs. Lise Marx, Los Angeles, California; Mrs. Elizabeth Mayer, Scarsdale, New York; Dr. Max Mayer, Scarsdale, New York; Dr. Alfred Merton, New York, New York; Professor Otto Meyerhoff, University of Pennsylvania Medical School; Professor Karl Neuberg, New York, New York; Dr. Peter Pringsheim, University of Chicago; Dr. Kurt Quasebarth, Great Neck, New York; Professor Fritz Reiche, New York, New York; Dr. Alfred Reis, New York, New York; Mrs. Eva Rost, New Paltz, New York; Dr. Karl Sollner, University of Minnesota; Dr. Barbara Spiro, University of Chicago; Dr. Andrew Szegvari, Akron, Ohio; Dr. Curt Wachtel, New York, New York; Mrs. Helene Weigert, Chicago, Illinois; Dr. Karl Weigert, Chicago, Illinois; Dr. Anna Weizmann, Northwestern University; Dr. Willis R. Whitney, Schenectady, New York; Professor Eugene P. Wigner, Princeton University; Dr. Walter Wolff, Philadelphia, Pennsylvania.

LETTERS

Dr. A. A. Benedetti-Pichler, New York, New York; Professor E. Berl, Carnegie Institute of Technology, Pittsburgh, Pennsylvania; Dr. Arnold Berliner, Berlin, Germany; the Honorable W. Boström, minister of Sweden; M. L. Bradford, managing director, University Arms Hotel, Cambridge, England; Professor G. Bruni, Milan, Italy; the Honorable Parker W. Buhrman, American consul general, Basel, Switzerland; C. F. Burgess, Chicago, Illinois; Professor J. E. Coates, Swansea, Wales; J. G. Crowther, London, England; Director, Federal Polytechnical School, Zurich, Switzerland; Director, Grand Hotel–Hotel Euler, Basel, Switzerland; Professor Octave Dony-Hénault, Brussels, Belgium; Dr. Abram Flexner, New York, New York; Dr. Walter F. Frankenburg, Lancaster, Pennsylvania; Mrs. Else Freyhan, Knowl Hill, England; John Gunther, New York, New York; Mrs. Charlotte Haber, Middlesex, England; Professor Louis Kahlenberg, Madison, Wisconsin; Professor Hartmut Kallmann, Berlin, Germany; Librarian, Franklin Institute, Philadelphia, Pennsylvania; Professor Alwin Mittasch, Heidelberg, Germany; Professor Walther Nernst, Berlin, Germany; Office of the Secretary, American Chemical Society, Washington, D. C.; Dr. R. Pirani, New York, New York; Sir William Pope, Cambridge, England; Dr. Kurt Semon, New York, New York; Professor Rudolf Staehelin, Basel, Switzerland; Professor Hugh S. Taylor, Princeton, New Jersey; Professor Max von Laue, Berlin, Germany; Dr. Pieter Zeeman, Amsterdam, Netherlands.

Articles about Fritz Haber

Acta. Chem. Fenn., "Obituary," 7A:21–32. 1934.

Alexander, Jerome. "Letter to the Editor," *Science,* 51:348. 1920.

"Anniversary of Professor F. Haber's Death," *Nature,* 135:176, 316. 1935.

Askenasy, Paul. "In Honor of Fritz Haber's Sixtieth Birthday," *Zeit. Angew. Chem.*, 41:1289. 1928.

"The Award of Medals of the Royal Society to Dr. Hale and Professor Haber," *Science,* 76:620. 1932.

Berl E., "Fritz Haber," *Jour. Chem. Educ.*, 14:203–207. 1937.

——— "Fritz Haber's Sixtieth Birthday," *Zeit. Elek.*, 34:797–803. 1928.

Bodenstein, M. "Obituary Notice," *Zeit. Elek.*, 40:113–15. 1934.

Bonhoeffer, K. "Obituary Notice," *Chem. Zeit.*, 58:118, 205–206. 1934.

Boyer, Jacques. "Obituary Notice," *La Nature,* 62:281. 1934.

Chem. Age (London), 5:370. 1921. 30:113 (Obituary), 1934.

Coates, J. E. "The Haber Memorial Lecture," *Jour. Chem. Soc.*, November: 1642–72. 1939.

"Critical Notes on Dr. F. Haber's Report on Electrochemistry in the United States," *Electrochemical Industry,* 1:385ff. 1903.

Crowther, J. G. "Fritz Haber is Clue to Germany's Revival," *The New York Times,* Sunday, October 19, 1930, sec. 9, p. 17, col. 1.

———. *The Social Relations of Science. Pages* 491–510. New York, Macmillan Co., 1941.

"Dubious Nobel Award," *Literary Digest,* 64:32–33. 1920.

"Editorial Paragraph," *Electrochemical Industry,* 1:380. 1903.

Electrochemical Industry, 1:58, 78. 1902. 1:340. 1903.

"The Extraction of Gold from Sea Water," *Science* (Supp.), 60: 10. 1924.

Franck, J. "Fritz Haber's Work on Stimulation and Ionization Through Chemical Reactions," *Naturw.,* 16:1071. 1928.

Freundlich, H. "Fritz Haber in the Karlsruhe and Dahlem Laboratories," *Naturw.,* 16:1065. 1928.

Goran, Morris. "Fritz Haber and the Nazis," *American Hebrew,* July 24, 1942, p. 5.

———. "Fritz Haber's Views of Early Twentieth Century United States," read before the American Chemical Society, Chicago, April 20, 1948. Goran personal files.

———. "Present Day Significance of Fritz Haber," *American Scientist,* July, 1947.

Harkins, W. D. "Kaiser Wilhelm Institute for Physical Chemistry and Electrochemistry," *Science,* 34:595–97. 1911.

Hevesy, G. von, and O. Stern. "Fritz Haber's Work in the Field of Physical Chemistry and Electrochemistry," *Naturw.,* 16: 1062. 1928.

Ind. Eng. Chem., 13:283–84. Editorial. 1921.

Jaenicke, J. "Haber's Research on the Gold Content of Sea Water, *Naturw.,* 23:57–63. 1935.

Journ. Soc. Chem. Ind., 37:13. Editorial. 1918. 53:1234 (Obituary). 1934.

Kallmann, H. "In Memoriam Fritz Haber," address at the 12th anniversary of the death of Fritz Haber. Berlin, 1946.

Laue, Max von. "Obituary Notice," *Naturw.*, 22:97. 1934.

LeRossignol, R. "The History of the Preparation of Synthetic Ammonia," *Naturw.*, 16:1060. 1928.

Lohs, Karlheinz. "An Exponent of Science," *Zeit. Geschichte Naturw.*, 4:37–44. 1964.

Mittasch, A. "Obituary Notice," *I. G. Farbenindustrie House Organ*, February, 1934.

Nature, 106:66. 1920. 132:890. 1933. 135:176, 216. 136:506. 1935. 141:929. 1938.

New Republic, 78:3. Editorial. 1934.

Norris, J. "Obituary Notice," *Proceedings American Academy Arts and Sciences*, 69:511–12. 1935.

"Professor F. Haber on Electrochemistry in the United States," *Electrochemical Industry*, 1:349–51. 1903.

Radio Broadcast. "The World is Yours," National Broadcasting Company, February 8, 1942.

Sauchelli, V., ed. *Fertilizer Nitrogen, Its Chemistry and Technology*. New York, Reinhold, 1964.

Schlenk, W. "Obituary Notice," *Berichte*, 67:30. 1934.

Science, 57:291–92. 1923. 78:460. 1933. 88:16 (Supp.). 1938.

Scientific Monthly, 38:292 (Obituary). 1934.

Slosson, Edwin E. "Notes on the Centenary of the Franklin Institute," *Science* (Supp.), 60:9. 1924.

"Statement from the Swedish Legation," *Science*, 51:208–209. 1920.

Stoll, A., ed. *The Memoirs of Richard Willstätter*. New York, W. A. Benjamin, 1965.

Terres, Ernest. "The Importance of Fritz Haber for Technical Chemistry and Chemical Technology," *Naturw.*, 16:1068. 1928.

Thorpe, T. E. "Letter to the Editor," *Nature*, 109–42. 1922.

Wansbrough-Jones, O. H. "Obituary Notice," *Nature*, 133:349–50. 1934.

Weizmann, C. *Trial and Error*. New York, Harper, 1949.

Willstätter, R. "To Fritz Haber's Sixtieth Birthday," *Naturw.*, 16:1053ff. 1928.

Wrangell, Margarethe von. "Fritz Haber's Importance for Agriculture," *Naturw.*, 16:1070. 1928.

Zeit. Elek., 4:32. 32:393. 1897. 8:356, 892. 1902. 75, 200, 448, 908. 1904. 11:284, 584. 1905. 12:24, 96, 196, 348, 616. 1906. 13:80, 484. 1907. 14:168, 220, 244, 319, 571. 1908. 15:472. 1909. 16:83, 183, 244, 960. 1910. 17:73, 484, 988. 1911. 18: 128, 1024. 1912. 20:470. 1914. 21:64, 308, 404, 590. 1915. 22:364, 408, 435. 1916. 23:104, 268, 323, 376. 1917. 24:145, 284, 360, 396. 1918. 26:251, 355, 356. 1920. 27:44, 47, 176. 1921. 28:289. 1923. 32:266. 1926. 33:79. 1927. 34:419, 675. 1928. 35:60. 1929. 36:55, 282. 1930. 37:119, 287, 380. 1931. 38:111, 398, 711, 761, 976. 1932. 39:59, 406. 1933.

NEWSPAPERS

Chicago Daily News, February 2, 1934 (Obituary by J. B. Wood), p. 2, col. 2. Monday, January 16, 1939, p. 2, col. 4.

New York Times, The, Thursday, April 11, 1918, p. 3, col. 7.
Saturday, November 15, 1919, p. 10, col. 7.
Monday, January 26, 1920, p. 1, col. 4.
Tuesday, January 27, 1920, editorial.
Sunday, September 25, 1921, sec. 2, p. 9, col. 2.
Monday, July 30, 1923, p. 13, col. 1.
Friday, September 19, 1924, p. 13, col. 2.
Monday, September 22, 1924, p. 9, col. 2.
Sunday, September 28, 1924, sec. 8, p. 6, col. 1.
Saturday, July 3, 1926, p. 28, col. 3; p. 38, col. 3.
Sunday, July 24, 1927, sec. 8, p. 10, col. 4.
Saturday, November 26, 1932, p. 13, col. 6.
Saturday, September 13, 1930, p. 18, col. 3.
Sunday, May 7, 1933, p. 12, col. 1.
Monday, January 21, 1935, p. 7, col. 4.
Wednesday, January 30, 1935, p. 6, col. 6.
Thursday, January 31, 1935, p. 18, col. 4.

Thursday, March 12, 1936, p. 20, col. 2.

Monday, March 11, 1935, p. 6, col. 4.

Monday, March 28, 1938, p. 7, col. 4.

Monday, October 31, 1921, p. 14, col. 2.

Sunday, January 28, 1934, p. 22, col. 6.

Sunday, July 22, 1934, p. 6, col. 4.

Sunday, January 12, 1935, sec. 8, p. 15, col. 1.

Thursday, November 5, 1925, p. 10, col. 2.

Sunday, October 25, 1925, sec. 2, p. 5, col. 7.

Friday, March 5, 1926, p. 2, col. 7.

Sunday, January 31, 1926, sec. 8, p. 14, col. 1.

Sunday, January 12, 1936, p. 31, col. 2.

Wednesday, February 7, 1923, p. 2, col. 2.

Sunday, July 15, 1923, p. 8, col. 1.

Sunday, September 7, 1924, sec. 2, p. 1, col. 8.

Friday, February 2, 1934 (Obituary Notice), p. 17, col. 8.

Trans-Pacific, The, Saturday, June 26, 1926, p. 5, col. 4.

Saturday, June 25, 1927, p. 17, col. 3.

Saturday, December 10, 1927, p. 16, col. 1.

Book Reviews

Aus Leben und Beruf. Physical Reviews, 30:358–59. 1927. *Zeit. Angew. Chem.*, 41:1327. 1928.

Experimental Inorganic Chemistry. By Alexander Smith; translated into German by F. Haber and M. Stocker. *Zeit. Elek.*, 9:929. 1903.

Experimental Studies on the Decomposition and Combustion of Hydrocarbons. Zeit. Elek., 2:667, 1896.

Festschrift der Kaiser Wilhelm Gesellschaft zür Foerderung der Wissenschaften zu ihren Zehn Jährigen Jubiläm. Nature, 109:69. 1922.

Outline of Technical Electrochemistry on a Theoretical Basis. Zeit. Elek., 4:556–57. *Jour. Gasbel.*, 41:536. 1898.

Thermodynamics of Technical Gas Reactions. Zeit. Elek., 11:519. *Jour. Gasbel.*, 48:904. 1905.

READILY AVAILABLE PHOTOGRAPHS OF FRITZ HABER

Chem. Age (London), 30:113. 1934.

Chem Eng., 31:495. 1924.

Chem. & Engr. News, 31:1012. 1953. 42:108. 1964.

Chem Industries, 3:150. 1934.

Die Naturw., 16:1052. 1928.

Die Umschau, 22:659. 1918.

Discovery, 7:297. 1946.

Electrochemical Industry, 1:78. 1902.

Fortune, 6:48. 1932.

Jour. Chem. Educ., 8:1. 1931. 14:203. 1937. 15:561. 1938.

Jour. Soc. Chem. Ind., 51:554. 1932.

Junk, Victor. *Die Nobelpreistraeger.* Leipzig, M. Winkler, 1930.

La Nature, 62:281. 1934.

MacCallum and Taylor. *Nobel Prize Winners.* Zurich, Central
    European Times, 1938.

New York Times, The. October 19, 1930, sec. IX, p. 17.

Physics Today, 1:December, p. 8. 1948.

Scientific Monthly, 38:292. 1934.

Smith, H. M., *Torchbearers of Chemistry.* Page 115, New York,
    Academic Press, 1949.

RELATED SCIENTIFIC ARTICLES

"Acetylene as Motor Fuel," *Dingler's Polytechnisches Journal,*
    334:50–51. 1919.

Alderson, Victor C. "German Technical Schools," *Chicago Inter-
    Ocean,* November 3, 1901.

The Association of Special Libraries and Information Bureau.
    Report of the Proceedings of the Fourth Conference. 32:
    347–49. 1922.

Auld, S. J. M. *Gas and Flame in Modern Warfare.* New York,
    George H. Doran, 1918.

———. "Methods of Gas Warfare," *Jour. Ind. Eng. Chem.,* 10:297.
    1918.

Baly, E. C. C. "Theory of Geometric and Stereo-Isomerism," translated by Dr. Clara Haber, *Zeit. Elek.*, 17:211 ff. 1911.

Berl, E. "Georg Lunge (1839–1923)," *Jour. Chem. Educ.*, 16: 453–60. 1939.

Berliner, A. "The Participation of German Savants in the Development of War Materials," *Naturw.*, 7:793–95. 1919.

Bernal, J. D. *The Social Function of Science.* New York, Macmillan, 1939.

Bosch, Karl. "On the Development of Chemical High Pressure Technique in the Building of the New Ammonia Industry," *Die Chem. Fabrik.*, 6:127–42. 1933.

Browne, C. A. "Some Leading Events in the History of Industrial Chemistry in America from the Earliest Colonial Settlements Until the Outbreak of the World War," *Ind. Eng. Chem.*, 18:844 ff. 1926.

Bunte, K. "The Ammonia Process of Professor Dr. Haber," *Jour. Gasbel.*, 53:868–69. 1910.

Caldwell, William E. "Gold Content of Sea Water," *Jour. Chem. Ed.*, 15:507 ff. 1938.

Cambridge Ancient History. Ed. by J. B. Bury *et al.* Vols. 5, 46, and 61. Cambridge, Cambridge University Press, 1927.

The Celebration of the Two Hundred Fiftieth Anniversary of the Royal Society of London. London, Oxford University Press, 1912.

Chandler, C. F. "Chemical and Technical Education in the U.S.," *Jour. Soc. Chem. Ind.*, 19:591 ff. 1900.

"The Chemical Industry in Germany," *Electro. Industry*, 1:430–31. 1902.

Christie, Trevor L. "The Kaiser in the Holy Land," *Saturday Review*, January 4, 1964.

Clogg, F. B. "Adolph von Harnack," *The London Quarterly Review*, 154:241–46. 1930.

"Courses at German Universities," *Zeit. Elek.*, 4:345. 1897. 4:457. 1898. 15:616. 1909.

Cowles, Virginia. *The Kaiser.* New York, Harper, 1964.

Crozier, W. "Giant Power and National Defense," *Annals Amer. Acad.*, 118:100–106. 1925.

Curtis, H. A., ed. *Fixed Nitrogen*. New York, Chemical Catalog Co., 1932.

De Launay, L. *The World's Gold*. New York, G. P. Putnam's, 1908.

"Disraeli," *Encyclopedia Britannica*, 14th ed., Vol. 3, p. 246ff.

Editors. "Chemistry and the Oceans," *Chem. Eng. News*, 42: June 1. 1964.

Engloff, G. "Motor Fuel Economy of Europe," *Ind. Eng. Chem.*, 30:1091–1104. 1938.

"The Electrotechnical Institute at the Grand Ducal Technical Hochschule Karlsruhe," *Zeit. Elek.*, 6:133–37. 1899.

Emmons, H. *Gold Deposits of the World*. New York, McGraw-Hill, 1937.

"The Enemy on Precedents for Poison Gas," *Illustrated London News*, 147:178. 1915.

"The Explosion at Oppau," *Jour. Soc. Chem. Ind.*, 40:381–82. 1921.

Falkenhayn, E. V. *The German General Staff and Its Decisions, 1914–16*. New York, Dodd Mead Co., 1920.

Farrow, E. S. *Gas Warfare*. New York, E. P. Dutton Co., 1920.

Feuer, Lewis S. *The Scientific Intellectual*. New York, Basic Books, 1963.

Fischer, Louis. *Men and Politics*. New York, Duell, Sloan & Pearce, Inc., 1941.

Fradkin, E. K. "Chemical Warfare—Its Possibilities and Probabilities," *International Conciliation*, No. 245 (March, 1929).

Frank, Philipp. *Einstein, His Life and Times*. New York, A. A. Knopf, 1947.

"Franklin Institute Centenary," *Chem. Met. Eng.*, 31:492–95. 1924.

"Freedom of Science and Learnings," *Nature*, 140:169–70. 1937.

Freundlich, H. "Letter to the Editor," *Naturw.*, 10:660. 1922.

Fries, A. A., and C. J. West. *Chemical Warfare*. New York, Mc-Graw-Hill, 1921.

"German Chemistry to the Front," *Chem. Zeit.*, 58:118. 1934.

"German Observations on Our Industries," *Jour. Ind. Eng. Chem.*, 6:32ff. 1914.

Gilchrest, Col. H. L. *A Conservative Study of World War Casualties from Gas and Other Weapons*. Washington, Government Printing Office, 1928.

Goerlitz, Walter, ed. *The Kaiser and His Court: The Diaries, Notebooks and Letters of Admiral Georg Alexander von Mueller, Chief of the Naval Cabinet, 1914–18*. New York, Harcourt, Brace & World, 1964.

"Gold in Sea Water," *Jour. Chem. Soc. Absts.*, 88:532. 1905.

Goldschmidt, H. "Nobelprisvinderen Fritz Haber," *Tidsskrift für Kemm.*, 17:January 15. 1920.

Goran, Morris. "The History of the Ammonia Synthesis," read before the 10th International Congress on the History of Science, Ithaca, New York, August, 1962. Convention Summary Volume, Paris, Hermann, 1964.

———. "In Appreciation of Herbert Freundlich," *Jour. Chem. Educ.*, August, 1941.

———. "Letter on Poison Gas," *New Republic*, May 18, 1942, p. 671.

———. "The Myth of Poison Gas," *Scientific Monthly*, October, 1941.

———. "Swastika Science," *Nation*, June 3, 1939.

Gray, G. W. *Science at War*. New York, Harper, 1943.

Great Britain Ministry of Munitions of War, Munitions Inventions Department. *Nitrogen Products Committee, Final Report*. London, H. M. Stationery Office, 1919.

Gregg, Alan. "The Essential Need of Fundamental Research for Social Progress," *Science*, 101:258ff. 1945.

Gunther, J. *Inside Asia*. New York, Harper, 1938.

"The Haber Process at Oppau," *Jour. Soc. Chem. Ind.*, 40:99. 1921.

Hahn, Otto. *Otto Hahn, a Scientific Autobiography.* Ed. and trans. by Willy Ley. New York, Charles Scribner's Sons, 1966.

Haldane, J. B. S. *Callinicus, A Defense of Chemical Warfare.* New York, E. P. Dutton, 1925.

Hanslian, R. *Der Chemische Krieg.* Berlin, E. S. Mittler & Son, 1937.

Harnack, A. V. "The Crisis in German Science," *Nation* (London), 32:347–49. 1922.

Hart, Liddell. *A History of the World War, 1914–18.* Boston, Little, Brown, 1935.

Hartshorne, E. Y. "The German Universities and National Socialism." Unpublished thesis submitted to the Division of Humanities, Committee on the History of Culture, University of Chicago, March, 1938.

Haynes, W. "Cartels & Consolidations," *Jour. Ind. Eng. Chem.,* 23:588–93. 1931.

Hendrick, Ellwood. *Modern Views on Physical Science.* Philadelphia, The Franklin Institute, 1925.

Hill, A. V. "Replies (to letter to the editor)." *Nature,* 133:291, 616. 1934.

Horner, J. "Industrial Advance of Germany as Seen Through British Eyes," *Cassirer's Magazine,* 25:515–25. 1904.

"Inauguration of the German State Council for Research," *Nature,* 141:655. 1938.

"Industrial Education and Industrial Conditions in Germany," *Special Consular Reports,* Vol. 33. United States Department of Commerce and Labor, Bureau of Statistics, Washington, Government Printing Office, 1905.

Ipatieff, V. N. *The Life of a Chemist.* Stanford, Stanford University Press, 1946.

"The Jewish Spirit in Science," *Nature,* 141:778. 1938.

Johnston, R. H. "The Development of Electrochemistry," *Columbia School of Mines Quarterly,* June, 1902, p. 262ff.

Jones, C. H. "Nitrogen Fixation by the Haber Method," *Chem. Met. Eng.*, 22:1071–75. 1920.

Jones, G. "Nitrogen: Its Fixation, Its Uses in Peace and War," *Quart. Jour. Econ.*, May 1920, p. 391–431.

Jost, F. "The Ammonia Equilibrium," *Zeit. Elek.*, 14:373–75. 1908.

Junk, Victor. *Die Nobelpreistrager.* Leipzig, M. Winkler, 1930.

Kaempffert, W. "Science Notes," *The New York Times,* Sunday, July 24, 1927, sec. 8, p. 10, col. 4.

Lamb, A. B. "The Fixed Nitrogen Research Laboratory," *Chem. Met. Eng.*, 22:977–79. 1920.

Laurence, W. L. "Bromine from the Sea," *The New York Times,* Sunday, August 20, 1933, sec. 8, p. 5, col. 3.

Le Blanc, M. "The Institute for Physical Chemistry and Electrochemistry at the Technical Hochschule of Karlsruhe," *Zeit. Elek.*, 10:238ff. 1904.

"Lectures at German-speaking Hochschule on Electrochemistry and Physical Chemistry," *Zeit. Elek.*, 10:296, 747. 1904.

Lefebure, Victor. *The Riddle of the Rhine.* New York, E. P. Dutton, 1923.

"Letter to the Editor," *Zeit. Elek.*, 8:890. 1902.

Loudon, J. "Technical Education in Germany," *Eng. News,* 62: November 30. 1899.

Ludendorff, E. V. *Ludendorff's Own Story.* New York, Harper, 1919.

Marionoff, Dimitri. *Einstein.* New York, Doubleday, Doran, 1944.

McConnell, D. "Chilean Nitrate Industry," *Jour. Polit. Econ.*, 43:506–29. 1935.

McConnell, R. E. "The Production of Nitrogeneous Compounds Synthetically in the U. S. and Germany," *Ind. Eng. Chem.*, 11:837. 1919.

Memorial Lectures Delivered Before the Chemical Society, 1893–1900. London, Gurney & Jackson, 1901.

Merz, August. "Early American Coal Tar Dye Industry," *Chem. & Eng. News*, 22:1275–79. 1944.

Mulhall, M. G. "Industrial Advance of Germany," *North Amer. Rev.*, 166:640ff. 1898.

Muller, U. *Die Chemische Waffe*. Berlin. *Verlag Chemie*, 1935.

"Nazi-Socialism and International Science," *Nature*, 136:927. 1935.

Nernst, W., and F. Jost. "The Ammonia Equilibrium," *Zeit. Elek.*, 13:521. 1907.

"Niagara Falls Meeting of the American Electrochemical Society," *Electro. Indus.*, 1:57. 1902.

Nitrate Supply Committee Recommendations on Synthetic Nitric Acid," *Jour. Ind. Eng. Chem.*, 9:829–41. 1917.

"Nitrogen Fixation," *Scientific American*, 136:274–75. 1927.

"Nitrogen from the Air and the British Government," *Science*, 51:323. 1920.

"The Nitrogen Industry," *Fortune*, 2:55ff. 1930.

Norris, J. F. "Manufacture of War Gases in Germany," *Jour. End. Eng. Chem.*, 9:817–29. 1919.

Norton, N. B. *In and Around Berlin*. Chicago, A. C. McClurg, 1889.

Noyes, W. A. "Biographical Memoir of Alexander Smith," *Nation. Acad. Science*, Vol. 21.

"The Oppau Explosion," *Nature*, 108:137, 152. 1921.

"The Ostwald Process for Making Nitric Acid from Ammonia," *Scientific American Supp.*, 76:162. 1913.

Perman, Edgar P. "Direct Synthesis of Ammonia," *Proc. Roy. Soc.*, 76A:167–74. 1905.

"Philipp-Lenard-Institute at Heidelberg Ceremonial Dedication," *Nature*, 137:93–94. 1936.

Polanyi, M. "The Potential Theory of Adsorption," *Science*, 141:1010. 1963.

Prentiss, A. M. *Chemicals in War*. New York, McGraw-Hill, 1937.

"Report of the Eighth Convention of the German Electrochemical Society," *Zeit. Elek.*, 7:605. 1901.

"Report of the Fifth Convention of the German Electrochemical Society," *Zeit. Elek.*, 4:506–13. 1898.

"Report on the Kaiser Wilhelm Gesellschaft," *Naturw.*, 22:337ff. 1934.

Roberts, A. A. *The Poison War.* London, William Heinemann, 1915.

Rose, T. K. *The Metallurgy of Gold.* London, Charles Griffin, 1937.

Roth, Walter. "Chemical Industry in Germany Reacts to Politics and Research," *Chem. Indus.*, 34:19ff. 1934.

"Science and Intellectual Liberty," *Nature*, 133:701. 1934.

"Science and State in Germany," *Nature*, 132:198. 1933.

"Scientific Situation in Germany," *Science*, 77:528–29. 1933.

"Scientific Worthies: Richard Willstätter," *Nature*, 120:1–5. 1927.

Scott, E. K. "The Manufacture of Nitrate from the Atmosphere," *Jour. Roy. Soc. Arts*, 60:247. 1921.

Slade, R. E. "On Sodium Aluminum Solutions," translated by Dr. Clara Haber, *Zeit Elek.*, 17:261ff. 1911.

Society for the Protection of Science and Learning. *Third and Fourth Reports.* London, July, 1937; November, 1938.

Stark, J. "Letter to the Editor," *Nature*, 133:290, 615–16. 1934. (See also A. V. Hill.)

———. "The Pragmatic and Dogmatic Spirit in Physics," *Nature*, 141:770–72. 1938.

Stewart, L. C. "Commercial Extraction of Bromine from Sea Water," *Jour. Ind. Eng. Chem.*, 26:261ff. 1934.

"Themistocles," *Encyclopaedia Britannica*, 14th ed., Vol. 22, p. 53.

Thwaite, B. H. "Commercial War Between Germany and England," *Nineteenth Century*, 40:925–31. 1896.

Time, 28:28ff. 1936.

Transactions and Organization, Eighth International Congress of Applied Chemistry. Concord, New Hampshire, Rumford Press, 1912.

Transactions of the American Electrochemical Society, Vols. 1 and 2.

Trautz, M. *Lehrbuch der Chemie.* Berlin, W. de Gruyter, 1922.

"Typical German Pronouncement," *Jour. Ind. Eng. Chem.,* 10: 420. 1918.

Senate Committee on Finance. *Hearings* on the Proposed Tariff Act of 1921 (H.R. 7456).

Urbain, George, ed. *La Sciences, Ses Progres, Ses Applicat.* 2 vols. Paris, 1933.

Washburg, F. S. "The Cyanamid Process," *Chem. Met. Eng.,* 13:745. 1915.

Wats, H. E. "Notes on the Nitrogen Position in Germany," *Chem. Age* (London), 8:226–27. 1923.

Weinberg, A. V. "Emil Fischer Andenken," *Naturw.,* 7:869. 1918.

West, C. J. "The History of Poison Gases," *Science,* 49:413. 1919.

Zanetti, J. E. *The Significance of Nitrogen.* New York, The Chemical Foundation, 1932.

Index

207

119, 122–23, 135, 139, 149, 151, 157, 166
Haber, Clara: 29–31, 32, 37, 71–72
Haber, Edward: 32, 88
Haber, Eva: 122, 166
Haber, Fritz: childhood, 4–5; friends, 4–5, 117–19; interest in dramatics, 5, 59, 83, 127; military service, 8–9, 66ff.; first research, 10; argument with father, 14–15; first research with Bunte, 20; books, 21, 26, 37, 142, 143; tall tales, 23, 58, 77, 121, 134, 139; uniting theory and practice, 26, 34, 35, 147; courtship of Clara Immerwahr, 28–29; views of the United States, 34, 145–46, 147–48, 149; as critic, 36, 104–105; as a Jew, 38, 40, 157, 167–68; genealogy, 39, 121; royalty arrangement, 52, 87; style of speaking, 56, 138–39, 140–42; relations with students, 36, 56–57, 58, 62–63; relations with son, 59, 89–90; health, 80–81; 131–32, 166; admits a mistaken view, 97–98, 129, 168; the colloquium, 103–105; attitude toward mathematics, 105, 108; choice of co-workers, 106–107, 161; research direction, 107–108; students examination methods, 109–110; attitude toward workers, 111–12; kindness, 112, 133; relations with colleagues, 114 ff.; attitude of public toward him, 120, 130, 169; relations with relatives, 120 ff.; relations with second wife, 122 ff., attitude toward women, 124, 165, 170; abilities, 126 ff.; comparison to other great men, 54, 127–28, 142, 163–67; working habits, 128; reading habits, 137; foreign travels, 146 ff.; international honors, 151–52; politics, 153–54; relations with Nazis, 159 ff.

Haber, Hermann: 32, 59, 78, 89–90, 116, 117, 118, 119, 121, 123–24, 153, 166, 167, 168, 170
Haber, Jacob: 39
Haber, Julius (uncle to Seigfried Haber): 38
Haber, Julius (brother to Siegfried Haber): 11, 40
Haber, Ludwig: 122
Haber, Ludwig (uncle of Fritz Haber): 149
Haber, Margaret Stern: 119, 121–22, 138
Haber, Paula: 4
Haber, Pinkus Seelig: 39
Haber, Siegfried: 14–15, 38, 40, 88
Haber, Solomon von: 40
Hahn, Otto: 174
Hamburg cholera epidemic: 15
Hamburger, Ernst: 5
Hamburger, Hedwig: 4, 38
Hamburger, Hermann: 14, 29
Hansa (ship): 94, 95, 111, 113
Harnack, Adolf von: 62, 141
Harnack House: 99, 106, 173, 174
Harteck, P.: 106
Hartley, Harold: 133
Hartmann, Max: 100
Harvey, Edmund Newton: 104
Hase, Albrecht: 104
Hausrath (friend at Karlsruhe): 22
Hecht, Selig: 104
Heine, Heinrich: 38
Henry, Prince (Heinrich Frederick Ludwig): 6
Helmholtz, Hermann: 6, 7, 61
Hertz, Gustav: 138
Hertz, Heinrich: 17
Herzog, R. O.: 100, 106
Hess, R.: 165
Hevesy, Georg von: 120
Hilferding, R.: 155
Hiller, Fritz: 58, 62
Hindenburg, President Paul von: 154